READABLE
RELATIVITY

HARPER TORCHBOOKS / The Cloister Library

Tor Andrae	MOHAMMED: *The Man and His Faith* TB/62
Augustine/Przywara	AN AUGUSTINE SYNTHESIS TB/35
Roland H. Bainton	THE TRAVAIL OF RELIGIOUS LIBERTY TB/30
Karl Barth	DOGMATICS IN OUTLINE TB/56
Karl Barth	THE WORD OF GOD AND THE WORD OF MAN TB/13
Nicolas Berdyaev	THE BEGINNING AND THE END TB/14
Nicolas Berdyaev	THE DESTINY OF MAN TB/61
J. H. Breasted	DEVELOPMENT OF RELIGION AND THOUGHT IN ANCIENT EGYPT TB/57
Martin Buber	ECLIPSE OF GOD: *Studies in the Relation Between Religion and Philosophy* TB/12
Martin Buber	MOSES: *The Revelation and the Covenant* TB/27
Martin Buber	THE PROPHETIC FAITH TB/73
Martin Buber	TWO TYPES OF FAITH TB/75
Jacob Burckhardt	THE CIVILIZATION OF THE RENAISSANCE IN ITALY [Illustrated Edition]: *Vol. I*, TB/40; *Vol. II*, TB/41
Edward Conze	BUDDHISM: *Its Essence and Development* TB/58
Frederick Copleston	MEDIEVAL PHILOSOPHY TB/76
F. M. Cornford	FROM RELIGION TO PHILOSOPHY: *A Study in the Origins of Western Speculation* TB/20
G. G. Coulton	MEDIEVAL FAITH AND SYMBOLISM [Part I of "Art and the Reformation"] TB/25
G. G. Coulton	THE FATE OF MEDIEVAL ART IN THE RENAISSANCE AND REFORMATION [Part II of "Art and the Reformation"] TB/26
H. G. Creel	CONFUCIUS AND THE CHINESE WAY TB/63
Adolf Deissmann	PAUL: *A Study in Social and Religious History* TB/15
C. H. Dodd	THE AUTHORITY OF THE BIBLE TB/43
Johannes Eckhart	MEISTER ECKHART: A Modern Translation TB/8
Mircea Eliade	COSMOS AND HISTORY: *The Myth of the Eternal Return* TB/50
Morton S. Enslin	CHRISTIAN BEGINNINGS TB/5
Morton S. Enslin	THE LITERATURE OF THE CHRISTIAN MOVEMENT TB/6
G. P. Fedotov	THE RUSSIAN RELIGIOUS MIND: *Kievan Christianity, the 10th to the 13th Centuries* TB/70
Ludwig Feuerbach	THE ESSENCE OF CHRISTIANITY. Intro. by Karl Barth TB/11
Harry E. Fosdick	A GUIDE TO UNDERSTANDING THE BIBLE TB/2
Henri Frankfort	ANCIENT EGYPTIAN RELIGION: An Interpretation TB/77
Sigmund Freud	ON CREATIVITY AND THE UNCONSCIOUS: *Papers on the Psychology of Art, Literature, Love, Religion* TB/45
Maurice Friedman	MARTIN BUBER: *The Life of Dialogue* TB/64
O. B. Frothingham	TRANSCENDENTALISM IN NEW ENGLAND: *A History* TB/59
Edward Gibbon	THE END OF THE ROMAN EMPIRE IN THE WEST [J. B. Bury Edition, illus., Chapters 36–43] TB/37
Edward Gibbon	THE TRIUMPH OF CHRISTENDOM IN THE ROMAN EMPIRE [J. B. Bury Edition, illus., Chapters 15–20] TB/46
C. C. Gillispie	GENESIS AND GEOLOGY: *A Study in the Relations of Scientific Thought, Natural Theology, and Social Opinion in Great Britain, 1790–1850* TB/51
Maurice Goguel	JESUS AND THE ORIGINS OF CHRISTIANITY I: *Prolegomena to the Life of Jesus* TB/65
Maurice Goguel	JESUS AND THE ORIGINS OF CHRISTIANITY II: *The Life of Jesus* TB/66
Edgar J. Goodspeed	A LIFE OF JESUS TB/1
H. J. C. Grierson	CROSS-CURRENTS IN 17TH CENTURY ENGLISH LITERATURE: *The World, the Flesh, the Spirit* TB/47
William Haller	THE RISE OF PURITANISM TB/22
Adolf Harnack	WHAT IS CHRISTIANITY? Intro. by Rudolf Bultmann TB/17
Edwin Hatch	THE INFLUENCE OF GREEK IDEAS ON CHRISTIANITY TB/18
Karl Heim	CHRISTIAN FAITH AND NATURAL SCIENCE TB/16
F. H. Heinemann	EXISTENTIALISM AND THE MODERN PREDICAMENT TB/28
S. R. Hopper, *ed.*	SPIRITUAL PROBLEMS IN CONTEMPORARY LITERATURE TB/21
Johan Huizinga	ERASMUS AND THE AGE OF REFORMATION. Illus. TB/19
Aldous Huxley	THE DEVILS OF LOUDUN: *A Study in the Psychology of Power Politics and Mystical Religion in the France of Cardinal Richelieu* TB/60
Flavius Josephus	THE GREAT ROMAN-JEWISH WAR, with *The Life of Josephus* TB/74
Immanuel Kant	RELIGION WITHIN THE LIMITS OF REASON ALONE TB/67

(continued on next page)

Søren Kierkegaard	EDIFYING DISCOURSES: A Selection TB/32
Søren Kierkegaard	THE JOURNALS OF KIERKEGAARD: A Selection TB/52
Søren Kierkegaard	PURITY OF HEART TB/4
Alexandre Koyré	FROM THE CLOSED WORLD TO THE INFINITE UNIVERSE TB/31
Emile Mâle	THE GOTHIC IMAGE: *Religious Art in France of the 13th Century.* Illus. TB/44
T. J. Meek	HEBREW ORIGINS TB/69
H. Richard Niebuhr	CHRIST AND CULTURE TB/3
H. Richard Niebuhr	THE KINGDOM OF GOD IN AMERICA TB/49
Martin P. Nilsson	GREEK FOLK RELIGION TB/78
H. J. Rose	RELIGION IN GREECE AND ROME TB/55
Josiah Royce	THE RELIGIOUS ASPECT OF PHILOSOPHY: *A Critique of the Bases of Conduct and of Faith* TB/29
Auguste Sabatier	OUTLINES OF A PHILOSOPHY OF RELIGION BASED ON PSYCHOLOGY AND HISTORY TB/23
George Santayana	INTERPRETATIONS OF POETRY AND RELIGION TB/9
George Santayana	WINDS OF DOCTRINE *and* PLATONISM AND THE SPIRITUAL LIFE TB/24
F. Schleiermacher	ON RELIGION: *Speeches to Its Cultured Despisers* TB/36
H. O. Taylor	THE EMERGENCE OF CHRISTIAN CULTURE IN THE WEST: *The Classical Heritage of the Middle Ages* TB/48
Paul Tillich	DYNAMICS OF FAITH TB/42
Ernst Troeltsch	THE SOCIAL TEACHING OF THE CHRISTIAN CHURCHES. Intro. by H. Richard Niebuhr *Vol. I,* TB/71; *Vol. II,* TB/72
E. B. Tylor	THE ORIGINS OF CULTURE [Part I of "Primitive Culture"]. Intro. by Paul Radin TB/33
E. B. Tylor	RELIGION IN PRIMITIVE CULTURE [Part II of "Primitive Culture"]. Intro. by Paul Radin TB/34
Evelyn Underhill	THE GOLDEN SEQUENCE: *A Fourfold Study of the Spiritual Life* TB/68
Evelyn Underhill	WORSHIP TB/10
Johannes Weiss	EARLIEST CHRISTIANITY: *A History of the Period* A.D. 30–150. Intro. by F. C. Grant *Vol. I,* TB/53; *Vol. II,* TB/54
Wilhelm Windelband	A HISTORY OF PHILOSOPHY I: *Greek, Roman, Medieval* TB/38
Wilhelm Windelband	A HISTORY OF PHILOSOPHY II: *Renaissance, Enlightenment, Modern* TB/39

HARPER TORCHBOOKS / The Science Library

Angus d'A. Bellairs	REPTILES: *Life History, Evolution, and Structure.* Illus. TB/520
L. von Bertalanffy	PROBLEMS OF LIFE: *An Evaluation of Modern Biological and Scientific Thought* TB/521
R. B. Braithwaite	SCIENTIFIC EXPLANATION TB/515
Louis de Broglie	PHYSICS AND MICROPHYSICS. Foreword by Albert Einstein TB/514
J. Bronowski	SCIENCE AND HUMAN VALUES TB/505
A. J. Cain	ANIMAL SPECIES AND THEIR EVOLUTION. Illus. TB/519
T. G. Cowling	MOLECULES IN MOTION: *An Introduction to the Kinetic Theory of Gases.* Illus. TB/516
W. C. Dampier, *ed.*	READINGS IN THE LITERATURE OF SCIENCE. Illus. TB/512
H. Davenport	THE HIGHER ARITHMETIC: *An Introduction to the Theory of Numbers* TB/526
W. H. Dowdeswell	THE MECHANISM OF EVOLUTION. Illus. TB/527
C. V. Durell	READABLE RELATIVITY. Foreword by Freeman J. Dyson TB/530
Arthur Eddington	SPACE, TIME AND GRAVITATION: *An Outline of the General Relativity Theory* TB/510
Alexander Findlay	CHEMISTRY IN THE SERVICE OF MAN. Illus. TB/524
Gottlob Frege	THE FOUNDATIONS OF ARITHMETIC TB/534
Max Jammer	CONCEPTS OF SPACE. Foreword by Albert Einstein TB/533
D. E. Littlewood	THE SKELETON KEY OF MATHEMATICS TB/525
J. E. Morton	MOLLUSCS: *An Introduction to their Form and Functions.* Illus. TB/529
J. R. Partington	A SHORT HISTORY OF CHEMISTRY. Illus. TB/522
H. T. Pledge	SCIENCE SINCE 1500: *A Short History of Mathematics, Physics, Chemistry, and Biology.* Illus. TB/506
John Read	A DIRECT ENTRY TO ORGANIC CHEMISTRY. Illus. TB/523
George Sarton	ANCIENT SCIENCE AND MODERN CIVILIZATION TB/501
Paul A. Schilpp, *ed.*	ALBERT EINSTEIN: *Philosopher-Scientist:* *Vol. I,* TB/502; *Vol. II,* TB/503

(continued on next page)

P. M. Sheppard	NATURAL SELECTION AND HEREDITY. Illus. TB/528
O. G. Sutton	MATHEMATICS IN ACTION. Foreword by James R. Newman. Illus. TB/518
Stephen Toulmin	THE PHILOSOPHY OF SCIENCE: *An Introduction* TB/513
A. G. Van Melsen	FROM ATOMOS TO ATOM: *The History of the Concept* Atom TB/517
Friedrich Waismann	INTRODUCTION TO MATHEMATICAL THINKING. Foreword by Karl Menger TB/511
W. H. Watson	ON UNDERSTANDING PHYSICS: *An Analysis of the Philosophy of Physics*. Intro. by Ernest Nagel TB/507
G. J. Whitrow	THE STRUCTURE AND EVOLUTION OF THE UNIVERSE: *An Introduction to Cosmology*. Illus. TB/504
Edmund Whittaker	HISTORY OF THE THEORIES OF AETHER AND ELECTRICITY: *Vol. I, The Classical Theories,* TB/531; *Vol. II, The Modern Theories,* TB/532
A. Wolf	A HISTORY OF SCIENCE, TECHNOLOGY AND PHILOSOPHY IN THE 16TH AND 17TH CENTURIES. Illus. *Vol. I,* TB/508; *Vol. II,* TB/509

HARPER TORCHBOOKS / The Academy Library

James Baird	ISHMAEL: *A Study of the Symbolic Mode in Primitivism* TB/1023
Henri Bergson	TIME AND FREE WILL: *An Essay on the Immediate Data of Consciousness* TB/1021
H. J. Blackham	SIX EXISTENTIALIST THINKERS: *Kierkegaard, Jaspers, Nietzsche, Marcel, Heidegger, Sartre* TB/1002
Walter Bromberg	THE MIND OF MAN: *A History of Psychotherapy and Psychoanalysis* TB/1003
Abraham Cahan	THE RISE OF DAVID LEVINSKY: A Novel. Intro. by John Higham TB/1028
Helen Cam	ENGLAND BEFORE ELIZABETH TB/1026
G. G. Coulton	MEDIEVAL VILLAGE, MANOR, AND MONASTERY TB/1020
Wilfrid Desan	THE TRAGIC FINALE: *An Essay on the Philosophy of Jean-Paul Sartre* TB/1030
John N. Figgis	POLITICAL THOUGHT FROM GERSON TO GROTIUS: 1414–1625: *Seven Studies*. Intro. by Garrett Mattingly TB/1032
Editors of *Fortune*	AMERICA IN THE SIXTIES: *The Economy and the Society* TB/1015
G. P. Gooch	ENGLISH DEMOCRATIC IDEAS IN THE SEVENTEENTH CENTURY TB/1006
Francis J. Grund	ARISTOCRACY IN AMERICA: *A Study of Jacksonian Democracy* TB/1001
W. K. C. Guthrie	THE GREEK PHILOSOPHERS: *From Thales to Aristotle* TB/1008
Henry James	THE PRINCESS CASAMASSIMA: A Novel TB/1005
Henry James	RODERICK HUDSON: A Novel. Intro. by Leon Edel TB/1016
Henry James	THE TRAGIC MUSE: A Novel. Intro. by Leon Edel TB/1017
Arnold Kettle	AN INTRODUCTION TO THE ENGLISH NOVEL: *Vol. I, Defoe to George Eliot,* TB/1011; *Vol. II, Henry James to the Present,* TB/1012
L. S. B. Leakey	ADAM'S ANCESTORS: *The Evolution of Man and His Culture*. Illus. TB/1019
Bernard Lewis	THE ARABS IN HISTORY TB/1029
Arthur O. Lovejoy	THE GREAT CHAIN OF BEING: *A Study of the History of an Idea* TB/1009
Niccolo Machiavelli	HISTORY OF FLORENCE AND OF THE AFFAIRS OF ITALY: *From the Earliest Times to the Death of Lorenzo the Magnificent*. Intro. by Felix Gilbert TB/1027
J. P. Mayer	ALEXIS DE TOCQUEVILLE: *A Biographical Study in Political Science* TB/1014
John U. Nef	CULTURAL FOUNDATIONS OF INDUSTRIAL CIVILIZATION TB/1024
Robert Payne	HUBRIS: *A Study of Pride*: Foreword by Herbert Read TB/1031
Samuel Pepys	THE DIARY OF SAMUEL PEPYS: Selections, ed. by O. F. Morshead; illus. by Ernest H. Shepard TB/1007
Georges Poulet	STUDIES IN HUMAN TIME TB/1004
Priscilla Robertson	REVOLUTIONS OF 1848: *A Social History* TB/1025
Ferdinand Schevill	THE MEDICI. Illus. TB/1010
Bruno Snell	THE DISCOVERY OF THE MIND: *The Greek Origins of European Thought* TB/1018
W. H. Walsh	PHILOSOPHY OF HISTORY: *An Introduction* TB/1020
W. Lloyd Warner	SOCIAL CLASS IN AMERICA: *The Evaluation of Status* TB/1013
Alfred N. Whitehead	PROCESS AND REALITY: *An Essay in Cosmology* TB/1033

READABLE
RELATIVITY

CLEMENT V. DURELL

FOREWORD BY FREEMAN J. DYSON

HARPER TORCHBOOKS / The Science Library

HARPER & BROTHERS, NEW YORK

TO

THE MEMBERS OF SENIOR BLOCK, DIVISION G

CLOISTER TIME, 1924

WHO HELPED TO WRITE THIS BOOK

READABLE RELATIVITY

Printed in the United States of America

This volume was first published by G. Bell & Sons Ltd., London, in 1926, and is here reprinted by arrangement.

First HARPER TORCHBOOK edition published 1960

FOREWORD TO
THE TORCHBOOK EDITION

by Freeman J. Dyson

I am happy that I was asked to introduce this excellent book to the American public. I had the good luck to spend my high-school years at the school where Durell was a teacher. This was a school which followed the European tradition of offering the stiffest possible intellectual training to a group of boys selected by stiff entrance examinations. The caliber of the teachers at that time compared favorably with that of the faculty of an average university. Indeed after two years in Durell's mathematics class I found the life of a student at Cambridge University quite relaxing.

Americans certainly do not need or wish to adopt the European high-school system, based as it is on segregating the bright children and making them work ferociously hard. Still, there is much in the European system which Americans could usefully borrow. Without any sacrifice of democratic principles, American children could benefit from being exposed to serious and scholarly text-books. We in the English high-schools took it for granted that there would exist for our use text-books written from an adult point of view and in an acceptable literary style. Such text-books did in fact exist because they were written by our teachers, and the best of the teachers were men with a deep knowledge of their subjects. In the field of mathematics the books were mostly written by Durell. "Readable Relativity" is one out of about fifty books which Durell wrote as a by-product of his vocation as a teacher. It is probably his finest work, and it is

v

certainly the best layman's introduction to relativity that has ever been written by anybody.

It was characteristic of Durell that nobody knew him very well. To us boys he was more of a legend than a man. He would come into his classroom at 7:30 on a raw spring morning and fling open the windows. If one of the boys ever had the temerity to complain of the icy wind that whistled through the room, Durell would only remark drily, "Put more clothes on," and continue with the lesson. We took our revenge in school-boy fashion by lampooning him in scurrilous verses, but it would be quite wrong to imagine that there was enmity between us and him. He was for us like a force of nature, neither loved nor disliked but universally obeyed and respected.

The atmosphere of hard work and pursuit of intellectual excellence in which we lived was so pervasive that we took it for granted. It hardly occurred to us that it had taken a lifetime of effort and struggle on the part of a few people like Durell to establish such an atmosphere. We worked like slaves at our books, because the pace was fast, the problems tough, and to fall behind would be to lose our self-respect. Durell showed no special interest in those of us who were more gifted than the others. All received the same share of his attention. Though I was certainly one of the abler students, I remember only one occasion on which Durell gave me special treatment. I had spent many hours worrying over a particularly rugged problem, and I had finally succeeded in solving it in a correct but inelegant fashion. After I handed in my solution, it came back to me with the single word "Terrible" scribbled over it in huge letters. That piece of paper I treasured for many years afterward, for I knew that to an average student Durell could not have been so merciless.

Durell wrote "Readable Relativity" out of his experience

in teaching relativity to a class of school-boys. This makes
it totally different from the many books which have been
written without such experience. Where other books are
vague, verbose and philosophical, Durell is precise, brief and
practical. School-boys are the best possible corrective to
pious inanities in any field.

In this Foreword I have tried to describe the kind of
person Durell is. I do not need to say more about his book,
because his own short Preface already gives the best possible description of it. Although I have presented Durell as
a formidable character (which he is), the reader of this
book will soon discover that he writes in a simple and
humorous style, with a lightness of touch which can come
only to one who is absolute master of his subject.

Institute for Advanced Study, Princeton
April, 1960

PREFACE

RELATIVITY without mathematics may be compared with " Painless Dentistry," or " Ski-ing without falling," or " Reading without Tears." Its ideas have, of course, been sketched in popular style by many writers, but *precision* can only be achieved by setting out the arguments in a mathematical form, and this precision is essential for a firm grasp of the fundamental principles of the subject. This book attempts to secure as high a degree of definition as is compatible with the standard of mathematical knowledge of the average person. The limitations this imposes are obvious, but inevitable if the subject is to lie within the sphere of general education. Given, however, this small amount of mathematical capacity and preferably also a willingness to work out a few numerical examples to test appreciation of the ideas peculiar to the subject, it should be possible to make Einstein's view of the Universe as much a part of the intellectual equipment of ordinary people as is that of Newton.

It is difficult to specify all the books from which I have received assistance, but mention must be made of Professor Nunn's *Relativity and Gravitation*, and Professor Eddington's *Space, Time, and Gravitation* and *Mathematical Theory of Relativity*; I am also indebted to Mr. Greenstreet for allowing me to make use of the articles in the *Mathematical Gazette* to which reference is made in Chapter II, and to Professor Eddington for information about the solar eclipse expedition of 1922. The subject-matter of the brief note on Mr. Adam's work on the spectrum of the companion star of Sirius is taken from Mr. Adam's published paper on the subject, which Professor Turner very kindly showed me. I have also to thank Mr. W. L. F. Browne for reading the text and making a number of valuable suggestions.

C. V. D.

February 1926.

CONTENTS

CHAP.   PAGE

I. THE PROGRESS OF SCIENCE.   .   .   .   I

II. ALICE THROUGH THE LOOKING-GLASS   .   .   11

III. THE VELOCITY OF LIGHT   23

IV. CLOCKS   41

V. ALGEBRAIC RELATIONS   53

VI. SEPARATION OF EVENTS   67

VII. THE FOURTH DIMENSION   81

VIII. MASS AND MOMENTUM   99

IX. GENERAL RELATIVITY   117

X. THE EINSTEIN TESTS   133

ANSWERS   145

READABLE RELATIVITY

CHAPTER I

THE PROGRESS OF SCIENCE

" We know very little and yet it is astonishing that we know so much, and still more astonishing that so little knowledge can give us so much power."—BERTRAND RUSSELL, *The ABC of Relativity*.

Our Outdoor World.

Every one nowadays has heard of Einstein and Relativity. The man in the street, however, still treats the subject more as a fairy tale or a mathematical jest than as a contribution to scientific knowledge and method which is as momentous (if it stands the test of continued scrutiny) as any that has ever been made. Relativity is a branch of physics, *not* of pure mathematics. Its conclusions could not, of course, have been obtained without the aid of pure mathematical reasoning of a difficult and abstruse nature, but the mathematical side is incidental : mathematics has merely supplied the machinery for working on the material available and the language for describing the result. *The material itself is the product of experiment, observation, and measurement*. The whole aim of Natural Science is to examine what is happening in our outdoor world, the Universe in which we live, and to construct the simplest set of suppositions which will cover all the observed facts.

The sole question, therefore, that arises is this : Does

Einstein's theory of Relativity give a more harmonious and adequate picture of what is observed to be happening in the Universe than any other alternative scientific theory dealing with the same data, or not ?

Many articles in newspapers and magazines seem to suggest that the Relativity creed contains such fantastic propositions that, however much they may appeal to philosophers, they cannot be taken seriously by the matter-of-fact individual who prides himself on believing only what he sees and distrusts suggestions which seem to contradict his own personal experience. It is therefore essential to realise that Einstein's theory stands or falls by observed facts : it aims at describing how things such as matter, time, and space do really behave. If, and when, any one can offer a simpler and more comprehensive account of the outdoor world than Einstein's theory is able to do, then Relativity will be superseded or modified. But at the present time it is contended that no other picture of the Universe, as adequate as Einstein's, exists. The story of scientific progress illustrates how indigestible new ideas are as a diet for plain, blunt men, but equally that those ideas which stand the test of time are easily assimilated by the plain, blunt men of a later date.

The Ptolemaic System.

Tradition suggests that *Pythagoras* (550 B.C.) was the first to teach that the Earth is a sphere, poised in space. This puzzled the man in the street in two respects : (i) How was the Earth supported ? (ii) Why did not people or things on the other side of the Earth, being upside down, fall off ?

Here, then, was one of the first of a series of shocks scientists have administered to common sense and will doubtless continue to administer as long as knowledge increases. But many centuries passed before the sphericity of the Earth was generally accepted, at any rate outside Greece ; in fact it needed the circumnavigation of the world to drive it home as a matter of practical experience. Even to-day there are some who still maintain the Earth is flat (cf. Kipling's story, " The Village that voted the Earth was Flat," in *A Diversity of Creatures*), just as there are others who still try to square the circle. The Greek scientists, however, waived criticism aside and proceeded to calculate the circumference and diameter of the Earth. *Aristotle* (350 B.C.) states that the mathematicians of his time made the circumference 400,000 stadia (probably about 40,000 miles), but a far more accurate result was obtained by *Eratosthenes* (250 B.C.), who gave the circumference as the equivalent of 24,700 miles and the radius as 3925 miles, a degree of accuracy far higher than the rough methods he employed justify ; it was in fact a lucky result. A later but less accurate measurement was made by *Ptolemy* (140 A.D.), whose treatise, largely astronomical, *The Almagest*, dominated scientific thought for the next fourteen centuries. The Ptolemaic System placed the Earth at the centre of the Universe, and regarded the Sun and the planets as moving round it in paths built up of circle and epicycles (*i.e.* circles rolling on circles) ; and although as time passed minor modifications were made to bring the theory into closer accord with observation, the general principle was accepted without question, till the time of Copernicus. It may be of interest to record that a contrary view had been put forward before Ptolemy's time. A certain *Aristarchus* of Samos (310–230 B.C.) maintained that the Sun was the centre of the world and that both the planets and the Earth moved round it. But this was far too advanced a doctrine not only for the common man but also for the scientists of his day ; it offended their sense of propriety in that it degraded the Earth from the central to a subordinate position in Nature, and it outraged common sense to suppose that the Earth, which, as they said, any one could see and feel to be at rest, was really travelling through space more than a million miles a day. [Eratosthenes estimated the distance of the sun as 80,000,000 miles.] We are all now so accustomed to think of the Sun as the centre of the solar system that it is difficult to realise what a shock the normal man received when the doctrine was first seriously propounded.

The Copernican System.

The theory of *Copernicus, De Revolutionibus orbium Coelestium*, was published in 1543. It regarded the Sun as at rest at the centre of the world with the Earth and the other planets moving round it in circular orbits. The laborious work of *Kepler* (1571–1630), although showing that the orbits were not circular, gave powerful support to the heliocentric principle of Copernicus by establishing that the planets could be regarded as moving in ellipses with the Sun at one focus, and that the sizes of the orbits and the times and rates of description obeyed two simple quantitative laws, which later on assisted *Newton* to formulate his law of Universal Gravitation. The invention of the telescope in 1608 led *Galileo* (1564–1642) to discover Jupiter's moons, and this small-scale model of the solar system convinced him of the truth of the Copernican theory. After much hesitation and with considerable trepidation, which after-events fully justified, Galileo published in 1630 an account of his discoveries and beliefs. His thesis was not only a shock to the man in the street but, unhappily for Galileo, a shock also to the Church. In self-defence, he begged his opponents to come and look through his telescope, but neither the professors nor the ecclesiastics would do so. He was summoned to Rome, an old man in feeble health, tried by the Inquisition, and

forced to " abjure, curse, and detest his errors and heresies."
He died, a broken man and blind, near Florence in 1642.
Einstein has good cause to be thankful that there is no
Inquisition in power to-day.

Universal Gravitation.

The work of Copernicus, Kepler, Simon Marius, and
Galileo was crowned by the publication of Newton's
Principia in 1685. The notion that bodies fell to the earth
owing to some form of attraction exerted by the earth did
not originate with Newton. His genius showed itself in
extending this idea to the whole Universe, formulating his
result in a single law, and verifying it by an examination
of the motion of the planets, comets, the Earth, and the
Moon. Newton's troubles lay with his brother-scientists,
not with ordinary folk, and many years of his life were
embittered by the professional controversies which the
Principia evoked. It has been said that there are comparatively few scientists who can, at the present time,
really understand the mathematical work which is the
scaffolding of Einstein's theory, but there were relatively
far fewer in Newton's day who could appreciate the
reasoning of the *Principia*; and of course a long time
elapsed before Newton's ideas became part of the equipment of the ordinary educated man, as they are to-day.

The Mechanics of Galileo and Newton.

It is necessary to state, however briefly, the fundamental
principles upon which Newton, using the observations of
Kepler and the ideas of Galileo, based his system of celestial
mechanics. He followed Galileo in saying that the nature
of a body is such that, if at rest it will remain at rest, and
if in motion it will continue to move uniformly in a straight
line, unless there is some external cause operating to produce a change. This is the *Principle of Inertia*, and to

the external cause he gives the name of *Force* and therefrom develops his idea of *Mass*.[1]

For the working out of his mechanics, he postulates:

(i) The notion of absolute time : time flows uniformly and without reference to anything else.

(ii) The notion of absolute space : a fixed standard of reference, immutable and immovable, enabling the position or motion of any object in the Universe to be determined. The Earth is not at rest, the Sun may not be at rest, but there is, so Newton says, something existing in the Universe which will act as a fixed frame for defining absolute position and absolute motion.

The normal man neither had nor has any difficulty in assenting to these suppositions ; in fact they seem so natural that he is shocked when asked to question them. The idea of universal gravitation was, on the other hand, far more perplexing. It appeared to involve the notion of " action at a distance," whereas everyday experience pointed to the belief that the action of one body on another was either caused by direct contact or some concrete connecting agency. Newton himself appears to have thought that further explanation was needed. To-day it is an idea that the normal man accepts without protest ; for him time and tradition have, as always, acted as the necessary shock-absorbers ; but none the less since Newton's time a succession of scientists has attempted by a variety of physical theories to bridge the gulf.

Measuring Instruments.

The human senses, unaided by mechanical assistance, are not adapted for making accurate measurements either of time or space.

TIME.—Our sense of duration for periods of any length depends mainly on whether our occupation is interesting

[1] Fawdry, *Readable Mechanics*, ch. vii.

or tedious : our estimate of short periods of time is often ludicrously inaccurate. This may be illustrated by testing the ability of any one to judge the length of a minute, ruling out, of course, the assistance that counting, either aloud or mentally, affords.

The use of the sun-dial, which treats the Sun as a clock, is known to date back to 1500 B.C. in Egypt, and according to tradition it was introduced into Greece from Babylon by *Anaximander* in the sixth century B.C. ; about this time also hour-glasses and water-clocks began to be made. Clocks depending on trains of wheels driven by a falling weight were used by the Romans in the sixth century A.D. The pendulum clock was invented by *Huygens* in 1673, ninety years after Galileo had discovered the isochronous property of a pendulum : Galileo himself used for his experimental work a form of water-clock [1] which gave surprisingly good results. The first ship's chronometer of a reliable nature was constructed by a Yorkshireman, *John Harrison*, in 1761. This was an invention of immense practical import-ance, as at that time ships at sea could only determine their longitude by means of a clock. Under present condi-tions it is of less importance, because Greenwich mean time is sent out by wireless at noon each day.

SPACE.—Any one who visits Oxford should go and see the Evans Collection of ancient scientific apparatus at the old Ashmolean. The delicacy and accuracy of workman-ship of the rulers, compasses, and astrolabes (*i.e.* instru-ments for measuring angles fixing the positions of the stars), some of which date back to very early times, can only be appreciated by seeing them. *Chaucer* wrote a treatise on the use of the astrolabe to make sure that his son should be properly instructed in its theory when he went to Oxford. The principle of the vernier, applied first to circular arcs, was discovered by a Portuguese

[1] Fawdry, *Readable Mechanics*, p. 62.

named *Nunes* in 1542, and rediscovered by the Frenchman *Vernier* in 1631.

Artificial Extension of the Senses.

No great advance was possible in astronomy until the invention of the telescope in 1608. Naturally such an instrument at once aroused widespread attention, and within a few years telescopes were being used by scientists all over Europe. It not only increased the range of observation in astronomy, but it raised the degree of accuracy of measurement to a level far higher than had previously been possible. Modern discoveries are largely the fruit of two other inventions : (i) dry-plate photography, and especially its application to astronomy; (ii) the spectroscope and spectrum analysis. It is outside the province of this book to give any account of the amazing variety of application and the remarkable refinements of measurement yielded by these methods of research. The important point to observe is that the increase of knowledge of the Universe is due entirely to the successive aids that inventions have given in supplementing the powers of naked eyes and naked hands. Without such assistance, our knowledge of the structure of the world would remain very restricted. Without a telescope, we can only see details of things in our immediate neighbourhood, and that only to a limited extent ; to fill in further detail, a microscope is necessary. Our ears only enable us to hear notes of limited pitch ; our eyes are sensitive to a range of colour far more limited than the range of the photographic plate ; if events happen too rapidly, our brains receive merely a blurred impression which it needs a slow-motion film to disentangle.

Common Sense.

Most of our outlook on life is coloured by the impressions we receive through senses, unaided by any artificial assistance. What we call a common-sense view of life is largely based on an acquaintance with things, confined in size between fairly narrow limits, restricted to small ranges of temperature and pressure, moving at low speeds and for short periods of time. It is not unreasonable to say that this gives us as true a view of the Universe as (say) a tourist could obtain of the interior of Westminster Abbey by looking through the keyhole of a side entrance. Successive inventions have enabled scientists to enlarge the keyhole, and perhaps at some future date will even throw open the door. If Science by its study of things very small and very large, very near and very distant, of temperatures very great, of velocities very high, is driven to conclusions which seem to violate our common-sense attitude, our keyhole notion of the Universe, it seems reasonable to treat it merely as one more shock in the succession which the man in the street has encountered and eventually absorbed. Nature is a conjurer for super-men. Generations of scientists have attempted to penetrate her secrets. Bit by bit the disguise is being torn away, but each new discovery seems only to open out fresh avenues demanding further exploration. Nature is a true woman, who will have the last word. Scientists of every age may well echo Newton's account of his own life's work : " I do not know what I may appear to the world, but to myself I seem to have been only like a boy playing on the seashore, and diverting myself in now and then finding a smoother pebble or a prettier shell than ordinary, whilst the great ocean of truth lay all undiscovered before me."

EXERCISE I

1. Why do you sometimes see on a cinematograph the wheels of a car rotating in a clockwise direction while the car itself is moving to the left ?

2. A stone is tied to the end of a string and is whirled round in a circle horizontally. In what direction does the stone move when the string breaks ?

3. If you assume that the earth describes a circle of radius 93,000,000 miles in 365¼ days, how many miles does it move in a second ?

4. Galileo found it easier to show that the acceleration of a falling body is constant by considering motion down a slope instead of vertically. How could a cinematograph operator improve on Galileo's treatment ?

5. If you drop a stone and a feather at the same moment, do they hit the ground simultaneously ? Is your answer consistent with the statement that the acceleration due to gravity is the same for all bodies at the same place, regardless of their weights ?

6. A camera photographs a 100 yards race for a cinema film, taking 150 exposures per second. They are reproduced on the screen at the rate of 15 per second ; how long, roughly, will the race appear to the audience to last ?

7. Describe a vernier, and show how one can be made to read correct to $\frac{1}{100}$th inch.

8. Taking the length of the Equator as 25,000 miles, find the error in miles of the longitude of a position on the Equator, calculated from the record of a chronometer, if there is an error of one minute in the time.

9. Eratosthenes found that the sun was in the zenith at Syene when it was 7° 12′ south of the zenith at Alexandria, which was known to be 5000 stadia north of Syene. What expression for the radius of the Earth can be deduced from these data ?

CHAPTER II

ALICE THROUGH THE LOOKING-GLASS

" ' I can't believe *that*,' said Alice.

" ' Can't you ? ' the Queen said in a pitying tone. ' Try again : draw a long breath and shut your eyes.'

" Alice laughed : ' There's no use trying,' she said ; ' one can't believe impossible things.'

" ' I daresay you haven't had much practice,' said the Queen. ' When I was younger, I always did it for half an hour a day. Why, sometimes I've believed as many as six impossible things before breakfast.' "—*Through the Looking-Glass*.

Can Nature deceive ?

The scientists, in playing their game with Nature, are meeting an opponent on her own ground, who has not only made the rules of the game to suit herself, but may have even queered the pitch or cast a spell over the visiting team. If space possesses properties which distort our vision, deform our measuring-rods, and tamper with our clocks, is there any means of detecting the fact ? Can we feel hopeful that eventually cross-examination will break through the disguise ? *Professor Garnett*,[1] making use of *Lewis Carroll*'s ideas, has given a most instructive illustration of a way in which Nature could mislead us, seemingly without any risk of exposure.

Ultimately, we can only rely on the evidence of our senses, checked and clarified of course by artificial apparatus, repeated experiment, and exhaustive inquiry. Observations can often be interpreted unwisely, as an anecdote told by Sir George Greenhill illustrates :

[1] *Mathematical Gazette*, May 1918.

At the end of a session at the Engineering College, Coopers' Hill, a reception was held and the science departments were on view. A young lady, entering the physical laboratory and seeing an inverted image of herself in a large concave mirror, naïvely remarked to her companion : " They have hung that looking-glass upside down." Had the lady advanced past the focus of the mirror, she would have seen that the workmen were not to blame. If Nature deceived her, it was at least a deception which further experiment would have unmasked.

The Convex Looking-Glass.

We shall now follow some of the adventures of Alice in a convex looking-glass world, as described by Professor Garnett. As a preliminary, it is necessary to enumerate some of the properties of reflection in a convex mirror. For the sake of any reader who wishes to see how they can be obtained, their proofs, which involve only the use of similar triangles and some elementary algebra, are indicated in Exercise IIB., No. 1, p. 20.

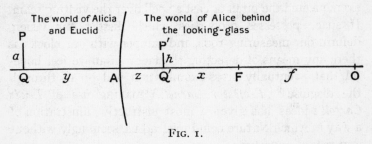

Fig. 1.

A is the apex of a convex mirror, of large radius ; O is its centre, OA is the central radius or axis ; the mid-point F of OA is the *focus*. PQ is an object outside the mirror, perpendicular to the axis and of height *a* feet, P'Q' is the image of PQ in the mirror. Denote the various lengths as follows, in feet :

$OF = FA = f$; $FQ' = x$; $Q'A = z$; $AQ = y$; $P'Q' = h$.

We have the following formulæ :

$$\frac{1}{z} = \frac{1}{y} + \frac{1}{f} ; \quad h = \frac{ax}{f} ; \quad x = f - z.$$

The general consequences of these formulæ are easy to appreciate.

Since $\frac{1}{z} = \frac{1}{y} + \frac{1}{f}$, we see that $\frac{1}{z} > \frac{1}{y}$, so that $y > z$.

and that $\frac{1}{f} < \frac{1}{z}$, so that $z < f$ or $z < AF$.

The image $P'Q'$ is therefore always nearer the mirror than the object PQ is, and is never as far from the mirror as F is.

Again, since $h = \frac{ax}{f}$, the height of the image is proportional to x, its distance from F, and therefore the nearer $P'Q'$ approaches F the smaller the length of $P'Q'$, the height of the image, becomes.

Life behind the Looking-Glass.

" ' He's dreaming now,' said Tweedledee : ' and what do you think he's dreaming about ? '

" ' Nobody can guess that,' said Alice.

" ' Why, about you ! ' Tweedledee exclaimed. ' And if he left off dreaming about you, where do you suppose you'd be ? '

" ' Where I am now, of course,' said Alice.

" ' Not you ! ' Tweedledee retorted contemptuously. ' You'd be nowhere. Why, you're only a sort of thing in his dream ! '

" ' If that there King was to wake,' added Tweedledum, ' you'd go out—bang !—just like a candle ! '

" ' I *am* real ! ' said Alice, and began to cry.

" ' You won't make yourself a bit realer by crying,' Tweedledee remarked."

We shall now treat Alice not as a thing in a dream, but as the image in a convex looking-glass of a pseudo-Alice who is moving about in our own world. Alice will insist as vehemently as she did to Tweedledee that she is a free agent with an independent existence, but we, looking from outside, will see that she conforms to the movements and amusements of this pseudo-Alice, whom we will call *Alicia*. We proceed to compare our (or Alicia's) observations with Alice's own ideas about her mode of life.

Alice's Life.

Alicia is 4 feet tall and 1 foot broad. She starts at A with her back against the mirror, so that she and Alice are back to back, exactly the same size. Alicia is carrying a foot-rule which she holds against the mirror so that it touches and coincides with, and therefore equals, the corresponding foot-rule which Alice has.

Alicia now walks at a steady rate of 1 foot per second away from the mirror, along the axis. What happens to Alice ?

Suppose the radius of the mirror is 40 feet, so that $AF = FO = f = 20$ feet. Then $a = PQ = $Alicia's height$= 4$ ft. After (say) 5 seconds, $AQ = y = 5$.

Then $\dfrac{1}{z} = \dfrac{1}{y} + \dfrac{1}{f} = \dfrac{1}{5} + \dfrac{1}{20} = \dfrac{5}{20} = \dfrac{1}{4}$.

$\therefore AQ' = z = 4$ and $x = Q'F = f - z = 20 - 4 = 16$.

$\therefore P'Q' = h = \dfrac{ax}{f} = \dfrac{4 \times 16}{20} = \dfrac{32}{10} = 3 \cdot 2$ feet.

If at this moment Alicia looks round, she will notice that Alice has only moved 4 feet compared with her own 5 feet, and that Alice's height has shrunk to 3·2 feet.

Alice's foot-rule, held vertically, has also shrunk : its length in fact is now $\dfrac{1 \times x}{f} = \dfrac{1 \times 16}{20} = 0 \cdot 8$ foot.

Alice repudiates the idea that she has grown smaller, and to convince Alicia she takes her foot-rule and uses it to measure herself, and shows triumphantly that she is still exactly four foot-rules high ($3 \cdot 2 \div 0 \cdot 8 = 4$).

Alicia also notices that Alice is not so broad as she was; her breadth, in fact, has now dwindled to 0·8 foot : true, the breadth is still equal to Alice's foot-rule, but that foot-rule in any position *perpendicular* to the axis is now only 0·8 foot long.

(For further numerical examples, see Exercise IIA., Nos. 1–3.)

Contraction-Ratio Perpendicular to the Axis.

We see that Alice continues to contract as she moves farther away from the mirror. The contraction-ratio in any direction perpendicular to the axis is $\dfrac{h}{a}$ which equals $\dfrac{x}{f}$ and is therefore proportional to x, Alice's distance from the focus F.

It is evident that Alice cannot detect this contraction, because Alice's ruler contracts in just the same proportion as Alice's body and Alice's clothes. In fact everything in Alice's world, regardless of what it is made, behaves in exactly the same way. We therefore call this contraction a property of space, not a property of matter. It is a form of influence which the space exercises on all things alike which enter it. And we say that *one of the laws of space in Alice's world is an automatic contraction-ratio which for any direction perpendicular to the axis, is proportional to* x, *the distance from the focus.*

Contraction-Ratio along the Axis.

Alicia now lays her foot-rule down along the axis, and of course Alice imitates her.

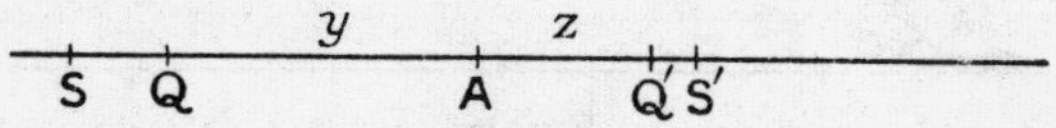

FIG. 2.

Q, S are two successive points of division on Alicia's foot-rule, such that AQ=5 feet, QS=0·1 foot, so that

AS=5·1 feet. The corresponding marks on Alice's foot-rule are Q′, S′. We have already proved that if AQ=y=5, then AQ′=z=4. Further, if AS=y=5·1, then AS′=z is given by

$$\frac{1}{z}=\frac{1}{y}+\frac{1}{f}=\frac{1}{5\cdot1}+\frac{1}{20}=\frac{20+5\cdot1}{5\cdot1\times20}=\frac{25\cdot1}{102}.$$

∴ AS′=z=$\dfrac{102}{25\cdot1}$=4·064, approximately.

∴ Q′S′=AS′−AQ′=0·064 foot.

∴   the contraction-ratio along the axis at Q′ is

$$\frac{Q'S'}{QS}=\frac{0\cdot064}{0\cdot1}=0\cdot64.$$

But the contraction-ratio perpendicular to the axis at Q′ has been shown to be 0·8.

Since (0·8)²=0·64, this suggests that the contraction-ratio along the axis is the square of the contraction-ratio perpendicular to the axis, at the same place.

Fig. 3.

The proof of this statement is indicated in Exercise IIB., No. 2. Alicia therefore notices that Alice becomes thinner from front to back as she moves away from the mirror, and the rate of getting thinner is more rapid than the rate of getting shorter.

For example, if Alice turns sideways and stretches out her left arm towards the mirror and her right arm away from it, the fingers of her left hand will be longer and fatter than those of her right hand, but the general effect will be to make the fingers of her right hand appear puffier—a chilblain effect—because these fingers have shortened more than they have thinned, compared with the other hand.

EXERCISE IIA

[In this exercise, Alicia is supposed to be 4 feet high and her waist measurement is 1 foot broad, 6 inches thick; also $f = 20$ ft.]

1. When Alicia has moved 10 feet from the mirror, show that Alice has only moved 6 feet 8 inches, and is now 2 feet 8 inches tall and 8 inches broad. What happens when Alice measures her height with her own foot-rule ?

2. When Alicia has moved 20 feet from the mirror, show that Alice has only moved 10 feet. What is Alice's height and breadth in this position ?

3. Where is Alicia, when Alice's height is reduced to 1 foot ? What is then Alice's breadth ? What is the length of her foot-rule, held vertically ? How many foot-rules high is Alice ?

4. With the data of No. 1, find the thickness of Alice's waist. What is Alice's measurement of it ?

5. With the data of No. 2, what is the contraction-ratio for Alice along the axis ? What is the connection between the contraction-ratios along and perpendicular to the axis ?

6. Alicia is 20 feet from the mirror and holds a 1-inch cube with its edges parallel or perpendicular to the axis. What is Alice holding ?

7. When Alice's height shrinks to 1 foot, what are her waist measurements ?

8. Does Alice's shape, as well as her actual size, alter as she moves away from the mirror ? When Alice's height has

dwindled to 1 foot, a statue is made of her on an enlarged linear scale, 4 : 1. Will this statue be a good life-size likeness of Alicia ?

Alice's Geometry.

While Alicia is walking away from the mirror at a uniform speed, taking steps of equal length, Alice is also walking away in the opposite direction ; but (according to Alicia) Alice's steps get shorter and shorter, and so she advances more and more slowly; and in fact, however far Alicia travels, Alice herself can never get as far as F. Alice of course imagines that there is no limit to the distance she can travel, and what Alicia calls the point F, Alice calls a point at infinity. If Alice walks along level ground, she imagines that the tip of her head and the soles of her feet are moving along parallel lines ; indeed the lines along which they move express Alice's idea of parallelism. Alicia sees that such lines actually meet at F.

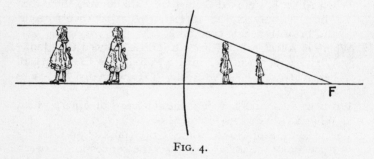

FIG. 4.

If Alice lays a railway track along the axis, the railway lines will behave in the same way.

Suppose Alicia is riding on a bicycle down the axis away from the mirror, how do the wheels of Alice's bicycle behave ?

The contraction is greater along the axis than at right angles to it. Consequently, not only are the wheels of

Alice's machine smaller than those of Alicia's, but Alice's front wheel is smaller than her back wheel : moreover, each wheel is approximately elliptical in shape, its vertical diameter being greater than its horizontal diameter, and although the wheels are turning round, the spokes which are vertical always appear to be longer than any of the others, and the spokes which are horizontal always appear to be shorter than any of the others ; the consequence is that the spokes appear to expand as they revolve from the horizontal to the vertical, and then to contract as they revolve from the vertical to the horizontal.

Fig. 5.

Alice herself, after careful measurement, is satisfied that the machine is quite normal, but Alicia will think it most unsteady. Space does not permit of any inquiry into the mechanics of Alice's life : for this, reference should be made to Professor Garnett's article, mentioned above.

Innocents at Play.

The object of this chapter is not to suggest that we are living in a looking-glass world, but to point out that there would appear to be no method of discovering the fact, if it were true. When Nature makes her laws of space, she can cast a binding spell over its inhabitants, if she cares to do so. But the fact that Nature is willing to answer some of the experimental questions which scientists put encourages them to think that gradually these laws of space and time may be disclosed. The purpose of this chapter will be served if it suggests that the search is not simple, and the results may be surprising.

EXERCISE IIʙ

1. BAC is a convex mirror whose radius AO is large compared with the object PQ. The ray of light from P parallel

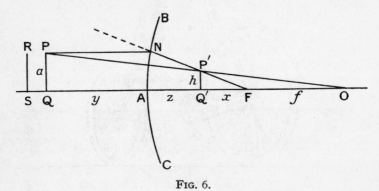

Fɪɢ. 6.

to the axis meets the mirror at N, and is then reflected along the line joining N to the focus F ; the ray of light from P towards the centre O of the mirror is not changed in direction by the mirror ; therefore the image of P is at the intersection P′ of NF and PO. Draw P′Q′ perpendicular to OA, then P′Q′ is the image of PQ. The focus F is at the mid-point of OA. Since the mirror has a large radius, its curvature is small, and NA can be treated as a straight line perpendicular to OA.

(i) Prove that $\dfrac{\text{FO}}{\text{PN}}=\dfrac{\text{FP}'}{\text{P}'\text{N}}=\dfrac{\text{FQ}'}{\text{Q}'\text{A}}$.

(ii) Hence, with the notation of p. 13, prove that

$$\frac{1}{z}=\frac{1}{y}+\frac{1}{f}.$$

(iii) Prove that $\dfrac{P'Q'}{NA}=\dfrac{Q'F}{AF}$ and hence prove that $h=\dfrac{ax}{f}$.

(iv) Hence show that $x=f-z=\dfrac{fz}{y}$ and that $\dfrac{z}{y}=\dfrac{x}{f}$.

2. If in the figure PQ moves along the axis a *short* distance to RS, and if the image of RS is R'S', and if $AS=y_1$, $AS'=z_1$.

use the formula $\dfrac{1}{z}=\dfrac{1}{y}+\dfrac{1}{f}$ to prove that

$$\frac{Q'S'}{QS}=\frac{z_1-z}{y_1-y}=\frac{zz_1}{yy_1}\frown\frac{z^2}{y^2}=\frac{x^2}{f^2}=\left(\frac{h}{a}\right)^2.$$

What do you deduce about the longitudinal contraction-ratio ? Those acquainted with the calculus should show that $\dfrac{\delta z}{z^2}=\dfrac{\delta y}{y^2}$, and interpret the result.

3. What does Alicia think of the movement of the hands of Alice's watch (i) when held facing the mirror (ii) when laid flat on the ground?

4. Alice spins a top so that its axis is vertical; what is there unusual about it, according to Alicia ?

5. The axis of the mirror A→O points due east. Alice, whose height has become only half that of Alicia, turns and walks north-east. What is her direction as measured by Alicia ?

6. Alice believes she has proved two given triangles congruent by the method of superposition. Does Alicia agree with her ?

CHAPTER III

THE VELOCITY OF LIGHT

" The first thing to realise about the ether is its absolute continuity. A deep-sea fish has probably no means of apprehending the existence of water ; it is too uniformly immersed in it : and that is our condition in regard to the ether."—SIR OLIVER LODGE, *Ether and Reality*.

The Ether.

Those who have engaged in physical research during the last hundred years have been rewarded by discoveries of far-reaching importance and interest. Light, electricity, magnetism, and matter have been linked together so closely that it now appears that each must be interpreted in terms of a single medium, the ether.

What the ether is will, no doubt, remain a subject of acute controversy between physicists of rival schools for many years to come. Its existence was first postulated to serve as a vehicle for light. Experiment showed that light travels through space at approximately 300,000 km. per second, thus light takes about $8\frac{1}{3}$ minutes to reach the Earth from the Sun.

According to the undulatory theory, light is propagated in the form of a wave motion through the ether. The work of Weber, Faraday, Clerk-Maxwell, and others established the remarkable fact that electro-magnetic radiation is a wave motion propagated with exactly the same velocity as light, and therefore presumably it uses the same medium as a vehicle. More recent research has shown that electric charges are discontinuous, and that the atoms of which matter is composed may themselves each be resolved into a group of electric particles; the group which constitutes each atom contains both negatively charged particles called electrons and positively charged particles called protons; atoms differ from each other according to the number and grouping of these particles. Each atom may be regarded as a miniature ultra-microscopic solar system, in which the electrons describe orbits round a central nucleus.

The ether is to be regarded as a *continuous* medium, filling the whole of space, and may indeed be identified with space: matter, electricity, etc., are *discontinuous*. But while identifying ether with space, we must also attribute to it some physical qualities in order that it may serve as a vehicle for physical phenomena. Some physicists credit it with weight and density. But if Einstein's view is accepted, it has no mechanical properties of this nature. Einstein holds that the idea of motion in connection with the ether is meaningless; the ether is everywhere and always. He does not say that the ether is at rest, but that the property of rest or motion can no more be applied to the ether than the property of mass can be applied to a man's reflection in a mirror, although the light-rays by which we perceive the reflection may and indeed do possess mass.

Absolute Motion.

If a passenger in a train observes another train moving past him, and if the motion is uniform and if there are no landmarks in view, it is impossible for him to determine whether his own or the other train, or both, are really in motion. This is a familiar experience. There is no difficulty in measuring the *relative* velocity of the two trains, but without a glimpse of the ground to act as a reference for measurement it is impossible to find what we tend to call the actual velocity of the train.

Again, suppose two balloons are drifting past each other above the clouds : an observer in one balloon tends to think of himself at rest and the other balloon as moving past him. Even when he obtains an accurate ground-observation, he can only calculate his velocity relative to the earth. An astronomer might continue the work and tell him the velocity of the observed point of the ground relative to the Sun and then the velocity of the Sun relative to one of the " fixed stars." But even all that will not enable him to find his actual or *absolute velocity*. What reason is there to consider any of the stars as fixed ? we know that they also move relatively to each other ; what indeed can the word " fixed " mean at all ? Is there anything in the Universe we can mark down as really fixed ? Scientists did not like the idea that all measurements of motion must be relative ; it seemed like building a structure of the mechanics of the Universe on a shifting sand. When, therefore, physical research demanded the existence of a medium filling the whole of space, the ether was welcomed not only for what it could do for light and electricity but because it appeared to offer a standard of reference for the measurement of absolute velocity. Scientists, therefore, set to work to measure the velocity of the Earth through the ether. The fundamental experiment which had this object, and which may be taken as the basis for describing Einstein's (restricted) theory of Relativity, was performed in 1887 by *Michelson* and *Morley*. We shall in future refer to it as the M.-M. experiment. The idea of that experiment may be easily understood by taking a simple analogy.

Rowing on Running Water.

A stream is flowing at 4 feet per second between straight parallel banks 90 feet apart. Two men start from a point

A on one bank; one of them T rows straight across the stream to the opposite bank at B and returns to A, the other L rows to a point C 90 feet downstream and then rows back to A. Each of them rows at 5 feet per second relatively to the water. Compare their times.

We have called the oarsmen T and L because T rows

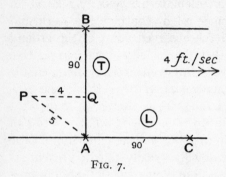

FIG. 7.

transversely to the stream and L rows longitudinally, in the line of the stream. Now T, in order to reach B, must point his boat upstream along a line AP such that if AP=5 feet (*i.e.* the distance he moves relative to the water in 1 second), the water will carry him down 4 feet from P to Q (*i.e.* the distance the stream runs in 1 second), where Q is a point on AB and ∠AQP is a right angle.

By Pythagoras, $AQ^2+4^2=5^2$, ∴ $AQ^2=25-16=9$,

∴ AQ=3 feet.

Therefore in each second the boat makes 3 feet headway along AB.

∴ the boat takes $\frac{90}{3}$=30 seconds to get from A to B.

Similarly it takes 30 seconds to return from B to A.

∴ the total time across and back=60 seconds.

Now L, on his journey to C, is moving relatively to the water at 5 feet per second, and the water carries him forwards 4 feet per second; therefore he advances at the rate of 5+4=9 feet per second.

∴ the time from A to C=$\frac{90}{9}$=10 seconds.

But when returning against the stream from C, his advance is only $5-4=1$ foot per second.

$$\therefore \text{ the time from C to A} = \frac{90}{1} = 90 \text{ seconds.}$$

$\therefore$ the total time downstream and up $=10+90=100$ seconds.

$$\therefore \frac{\text{time of L down and up}}{\text{time of T across and back}} = \frac{100}{60} = \frac{5}{3}.$$

It therefore takes longer to go down and up than an equal distance across and back. But the working of this example also shows that if we know the rate of rowing relative to the water, and if we know the ratio of the times taken for equal journeys in the two directions, we can calculate the velocity of the stream.

The Michelson-Morley Experiment.

It is known by experiment that light always travels through the ether at a constant rate of 300,000 km. per second. Let us suppose that at a certain moment the Earth is moving through the ether at a speed of u km. per second in the direction C→A, then from the point of view of a man on the Earth the ether is streaming past A in the direction A→C at u km. per second. AC and AB are two rigid equal and perpendicular rods, with

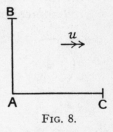

FIG. 8.

mirrors attached at C, B, so as to face A. At the same moment rays of light are dispatched from A, one along AC and the other along AB ; these rays impinge on the mirrors and are reflected back to A. The motion of these rays corresponds to the motion of the boats in the example given above. Each ray travels at 300,000 km. per second relative to the ether-stream, since its mode of propagation is a wave in the ether, just as each boat moves at 5 feet per second relative to the water. Also the ether-stream is itself moving in the direction A→C at u km. per second, just as the water-stream is flowing at 4 feet per second.

Now it takes longer to go any given distance downstream and back than to go the same distance across the stream and back. Consequently the ray from C should arrive back at A later than the ray from B. If then we measure the ratio of the times taken by the two rays, we can calculate the speed u km. per second of the ether-stream, and this is equal and opposite to the velocity of the Earth through the ether.

The M.-M. experiment was designed to measure the ratio of these times : for a detailed account of the apparatus employed, reference may be made to any standard modern text-book on light. To the astonishment of the experimenters, the race proved to be a dead heat, the ray from C arriving back at A simultaneously with the ray from B.

Now the earth is describing its orbit round the Sun at a speed approximately of 30 km. per second, consequently

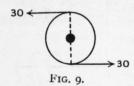

FIG. 9.

there is a difference of speed after a six months' interval of about 60 km. per second, so that even if the Earth should happen to be at rest in the ether at one moment, it could not be still at rest six months later. But the repetition of the experiment after a six months' interval still gave a dead heat.

Also, in order to guard against any error arising from an inequality of the lengths of the arms AB and AC, the experiment was repeated after rotating the arms so that AB lay along the supposed stream and AC across it ; but no difference of time was detected. Further, different directions were tried for AB, but without any result. The experiment has been carried out more recently with such added refinements that as small a speed as $\frac{1}{5}$ km. per second would have been detected. Here, then, was an experimental result which contradicted a conclusion obtained by theory. Clearly there was something wrong with the theory. Scientists were compelled to look for some explanation or some modification of the theory which would reconcile calculation with observation.

What is the Answer to the Riddle?

Let us return to the illustration of the boats which correspond to the light-rays in the M.-M. experiment. The two boats start together under the conditions stated on p. 26, and every one is then amazed to see them arrive back simultaneously. How is this to be reconciled with the conclusions reached by calculation?

The first suggestion is that L rowed faster relatively to the water than T; this, however, must be rejected because the speed of rowing through the water corresponds in the M.-M. experiment to the velocity of light through the ether, which we know is a constant, 300,000 km. per second.

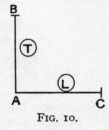

FIG. 10.

The next suggestion is that the courses are marked out incorrectly, and that the length of AC is less than that of AB, owing to careless measurement. But this view is untenable, because in the M.-M. experiment when the rigid arms AB and AC were interchanged, there was still no difference of time.

Fitzgerald then suggested that the arms AB and AC were unequal, not through faulty measurement, but because the shifting of a bar from a position across the stream to a position along the stream caused automatically a contraction in the length of the bar. The adventures of Alice have shown us that such a contraction could not be discovered by measurement, because the foot-rule with which AC is measured contracts in just the same proportion as the arm.

Suppose in the example of the boats the rule which measures 1 foot across the stream contracts to $\frac{3}{5}$ foot when in the line of the stream. When we measure out 90 foot-rule lengths to obtain AC, the outsider (Alicia) will say that AC is really $\frac{3}{5} \times 90 = 54$ feet, instead of 90 feet. L will then take $\frac{54}{9} = 6$ seconds to go downstream and $\frac{54}{1} = 54$ seconds to return upstream, so that his total time will be $6 + 54 = 60$ seconds, which is precisely the time taken by T.

This hypothetical phenomenon is called the " *Fitzgerald Contraction.*" Its value depends, of course, on the velocity of the stream ; when the stream runs at 4 feet per second and the speed of the rowing is 5 feet per second, the contraction ratio has been shown to be $\sqrt{\left(1 - \frac{4^2}{5^2}\right)} = \sqrt{\left(\frac{9}{25}\right)}$ $= \frac{3}{5}$. The reader will see, from this way of writing it, what its value would be in other cases.

In 1905, an alternative explanation was offered by Einstein.

Einstein's Hypothesis.

Einstein lays down two general principles or axioms :

(i) It is impossible to detect uniform motion through the ether.

(ii) In all forms of wave motion, the velocity of propagation of the wave is independent of the velocity of the source.

Let us consider what these axioms mean.

(i) There is no difficulty in measuring the velocity of one body relative to another : all our ideas of velocity are essentially ideas of relative velocity, either velocities of other things relative to ourselves or our own velocity relative to something else—*e.g.* a man who looks at the road along which he is driving his car is probably estimating his own velocity relative to the road. But it is meaningless to inquire what our velocity is relative to the ether ; no part of the ether can be distinguished from any other part : it may be possible to identify matter in the ether, but the ether itself defies identification. And if the ether cannot be (so to speak) labelled anywhere, the statement that a body is moving through it carries no information with it, or in other words has no meaning attaching to it.

(ii) The second axiom is perhaps more tangible. Imagine an engine moving at a uniform rate along a straight railway line on a perfectly calm day. If the engine-driver throws a stone forwards, a man on the line will observe that the velocity of the stone is equal to the velocity given it by the thrower+the velocity of the engine. The faster the engine is moving, the faster the stone will move, although the thrower exerts the same effort as before. The velocity of the stone relative to the air, therefore, depends on the velocity of the source, namely, the man on the engine.

Suppose now the engine whistles, and is heard by a man farther down the line. We know that the sound travels in the form of a wave through the air at approximately 1100 feet per second. But the motion of the sound-wave is a different type of motion from that of the stone : its velocity of propagation through the air does not depend on the velocity of the engine at the moment it whistled, *i.e.* it does not depend on the velocity of the source. The speed of the train will affect the pitch of the sound-wave, its musical note ; but the time the wave takes to reach the man is not affected by the rate at which the engine is moving. If, then, a particle in motion sends out a beam of light, the rate of propagation of the light-wave through the ether has no connection with the velocity of the particle which emitted the beam of light.

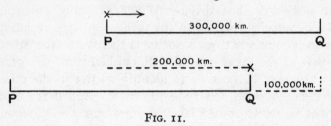

FIG. 11.

P and Q represent two places 300,000 km. apart and rigidly connected together. I take up my position at P and send a ray of light along PQ and measure the time it takes to reach Q. If PQ is fixed in the ether (assuming for the moment this phrase has a meaning), the time will be 1 second. If, however, my observations give the time as (say) only $\frac{2}{3}$ second, I can calculate that the ray itself only advanced $\frac{2}{3} \times 300,000 = 200,000$ km. through the ether, and that therefore Q must have advanced $300,000 - 200,000 = 100,000$ km. to meet it in the same time, $\frac{2}{3}$ second. Consequently the rigid bar PQ is moving at the rate of $100,000 \div \frac{2}{3} = 150,000$ km. per second. But as I remain at P, I deduce that my velocity through the ether is also 150,000 km. per second. This, however, contradicts Axiom (i), which lays down that a discovery of this nature is impossible. We are, therefore, forced to conclude that the measurement of the time of flight over this distance will always under all conditions be 1 second. Einstein's two axioms taken together, therefore, involve the following important result :.

Any one who measures experimentally the velocity of light in a vacuum will always obtain the same result (within, of course, the limits of error imposed by the experiment). The velocity of light in a vacuum, as determined by every individual, is an absolute constant.

This conclusion may well cause a shock to any one who considers carefully what it implies ; and the shock will not be diminished by examining its bearing on the problem of the boats.

It is, of course, important to notice the fundamental distinction between light-waves in the ether and sound-waves in the air. If an observer, when measuring the velocity of sound, obtains an answer which does not agree with the standard answer (about 1100 feet per second), he can at once calculate his velocity through the air. Nor is there any reason why he should not be able to do so ; and he can compare his result with that obtained by other methods. But with the ether it is otherwise; the inability of an observer to measure his velocity through the ether involves the fact that his measure of the velocity of a light-wave must agree with the standard measurement.

The Application of Einstein's Hypothesis.

No one can be conscious of moving through the ether. An onlooker O has no difficulty in measuring the speed at which a man L is moving away from him ; it will be equal and opposite to the velocity with which L calculates that O is moving away from him : if each expresses his measure of this velocity as a fraction of the velocity of light, the results obtained by O and L will be numerically equal and opposite in sign. Relative velocities, therefore, present no difficulty. But O and L alike will each consider himself at rest in the ether and will make his own measurements on that assumption. They, therefore, must be regarded as looking at the world from different points of view.

To explain the enigma of the boats, we must, therefore, consider separately the standpoint of each of the actors in the drama, the oarsmen T and L and an onlooker O, whom we will regard as poised just above T and L at the moment they start rowing. To make the analogy with the M.-M. experiment closer, imagine that the river-banks have disappeared, and that all we can see is an expanse of water devoid of all features or landmarks—that is what the ether-idea requires.

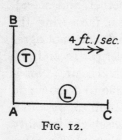

FIG. 12.

O says that this featureless ocean is moving in the direction A→C at 4 feet per second; in proof of this statement, he places a piece of cork on the water and observes that it at once moves away from him in the direction AC at 4 feet per second. T and L say that the water is motionless; each, sitting in his boat, places a piece of cork on the water and it remains where they have placed it; O, of course, says that these pieces of cork are drifting at the same rate as the boats. Further, T and L agree that O is moving away from them in the direction C→A at the rate of 4 feet per second; they say that the piece of cork which O has dropped remains stationary, and that it is O who is moving away from it.

The statement that the velocity of light is an absolute constant, or that each person who measures it obtains the same answer as any one else, when applied to the boats, means that T, L, and O will each obtain the same result when they measure the speed at which each boat is rowed through the water, because the boats are replacing the light-rays in the M.-M. experiment. We have taken this common measure of the speed as 5 feet per second.

Under these circumstances, our problem is to explain a definite experimental observation, namely, the fact that the boats (*i.e.* the light-rays) do return to A at the same moment.

Regard AB and AC as rigid planks of wood floating on

the water. T and L believe that these planks are at rest,
just as they believe the water is at rest ; O believes that
the planks are drifting with the water, just as T and L
are doing.

T, L, and O each have a foot-rule; T holds his along
AB, and L holds his along AC. O compares his foot-rule
with T's by actual superposition, and they note that the
two rules agree. As long as T's rule is kept perpendicular
to the stream, it will remain identical with O's rule; but
we shall see that when L, after comparing his rule with
T's, places it along AC in the line of the stream, *O will
consider* it to contract although *both L and T* are unconscious that it does so, and must remain unconscious of
this fact, because they can have no knowledge of the
existence of any stream carrying them along.

With the data of the problem, T and L satisfy themselves
by direct measurement that AB and AC are each 90 foot-
rules long. T and L, neither of whom recognise the existence of a stream, then calculate that their times to B,
C respectively and back to A will be in each case $\dfrac{2 \times 90}{5}$
=36 seconds. And their clocks must bear this out when
the trips have been made, for otherwise they could infer
the influence of a stream and calculate its velocity.

O now times T's trip. By the argument on p. 26, he
sees that T makes a headway of 3 feet per second along
AB and back, and therefore takes $\dfrac{2 \times 90}{3}$=60 seconds for
the whole journey. Consequently O says that T's clock
only registers 36 seconds when it should register 60 seconds ;
therefore, according to O, T's clock loses.

Now L and T take precisely equal times for their trips.
Therefore, by O's clock, L also takes 60 seconds. But by
the argument on p. 26, O sees that L advances at 9 feet
per second from A to C, and returns from C to A at 1 foot

per second. Therefore if AC=90 feet, the total time
$=\dfrac{90}{9}+\dfrac{90}{1}=$10+90=100 seconds; but the total time
according to O is only 60 seconds.

∴ according to O, the length of AC is only $\dfrac{60}{100} \times 90$

$=$54 feet.

[As a check, note that $\dfrac{54}{9}+\dfrac{54}{1}=$6+54=60 seconds.]

It is true that L marked out AC by taking 90 of his foot-rule lengths; therefore O is forced to conclude that L's foot-rule is only $\dfrac{54}{90}=\frac{3}{5}$ foot long, and so O says that the stream causes L's foot-rule, when placed along it, to contract to $\frac{3}{5}$ foot.

Further, as L also records the time of his trip as 36 seconds, O says that L's clock loses at just the same rate as T's clock. We may summarise these results as follows :

O *says* that (i) clocks in the world of T and L lose time ; they register an interval which is really 5 minutes long as only 3 minutes (60 : 36=5 : 3) ;

(ii) a foot-rule in the world of T and L measures 1 foot when placed along AB at right angles to the stream, but only measures $\frac{3}{5}$ foot when placed along AC in the line of the stream.

T and L say that (i) their clocks keep normal time ;

(ii) their foot-rules remain 1 foot long, in whatever position they are placed.

Who is Right ?

It seems absurd to suggest that all of them are right. Let us, however, inquire what L thinks about O. Suppose that O and his brother O′ mark out two courses, AB and AD, each of length 90 feet, along CA produced and AB, in the air just above the ocean.

Then L says there is a current in the air of 4 feet per second which carries O and O′ in the direction C→A ;

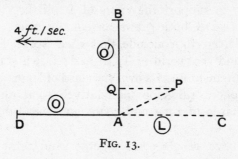

Fig. 13.

O and O′, of course, say that the air is at rest and that L is drifting with the water in the direction A→C at 4 feet per second.

Suppose now that O and O′ fly through the air at 5 feet per second (*i.e.* relatively to the air). O′ flies to B and back again to A, O starts at the same time as O′ and flies to D and back again to A. They both arrive back at A at the same moment. This is the experimental fact established in the M.-M. experiment, which needs explanation.

It is clear that L's views (or T's views) about O and O′ are precisely the same as those which O formed about T and L. The arithmetical calculations are identical and need not be repeated. The results may be expressed as follows :

> *L and T say* that (i) clocks in the world of O and O′ lose time ; they register an interval which is really 5 minutes long as only 3 minutes ;
>
> (ii) a foot-rule in the world of O and O′ measures 1 foot when placed along AB at right angles to the current, but only measures $\frac{3}{5}$ foot when placed along AD in the line of the current.
>
> *O and O′ say* that (i) their clocks keep normal time ;
>
> (ii) their foot-rules remain 1 foot long, in whatever position they are placed.

It is clear, therefore, that any argument that can be used to support the views of O or O′ can be applied with equal force to support the views of T and L. We must, therefore, regard both views as equally true. We are therefore forced to conclude that each world, the world of O, O′, and the world of T, L, has its own standard of time-measurement and its own standard of length-measurement. If one world is moving relatively to another world, their standards of time and space automatically become different.

Suppose two people come together and compare their clocks to make sure they run at the same rate, and compare their foot-rules to make sure they agree, and suppose that afterwards they separate at a uniform rate, one from the other, along a line AC. Now imagine two explosions to take place at different times at different places somewhere on AC. Each observer, making proper allowance for the time sound takes to travel, can measure the time-interval between the two events and the distance-interval of the spots at which they occurred. But their measurements will not agree, either as regards time-interval or as regards distance-interval, for they have different standards of time and different standards of length.

There is indeed one measurement about which they will agree, namely, the velocity of a ray of light : each of them, using his own clock and his own rule, will find experimentally that a light-wave travels at 300,000 km. per second.

NOTE.—The statement (see p. 28) that further repetitions of the M.-M. experiment have confirmed the conclusion that no ether-stream can be detected requires some qualification. In a repetition of the M.-M experiment in 1925, Professor Dayton Miller believed that he had been able to measure a drift which varied from zero at sea-level up to 10 km. per second at the summit of Mount Wilson.

No satisfactory explanation of these small velocities has been given, but probably they are due to the nature of the apparatus rather than to the existence of an ether. The problem is under study by Dr. Essen at the National Physical Laboratory, using electro-magnetic radiation of wave-length different from that of light-waves, which is likely to give results of greater accuracy.

EXERCISE III

1. A man's foot-rule is really only 10 inches long; what is the true length of a fence which the man measures as 12 yards? What will the man say is the length of a fence whose true length is 20 yards?

2. A foot-rule contracts to $\frac{3}{4}$ of its proper length. What is the true length of a line which according to this foot-rule is y feet? If the foot-rule is used to measure the length of a line whose true length is z feet, what result is obtained?

3. O says that two events occurred at an interval of 12 seconds at places 18 feet apart. What measurements are given by L, if his clock only registers 45 minutes for each hour of O's clock, and if his foot-rule only measures 8 inches according to O's rule?

4. A stream flows at 3 feet per second, and a man can row at 5 feet per second through the water. The width of the stream is 40 feet. Find the times taken to row (i) straight across the stream and back, (ii) 40 feet downstream and back.

5. With the data of No. 4, find how far the man can row downstream and back if he takes the same time as he would to go straight across and back.

6. It is found that a bullet from a rifle travels 1100 feet in the first second of motion. The bullet is fired along a railway line from a train at a moment when a man is 1100 feet away in the line of fire. There is no wind. Does the bullet or the noise of the explosion reach the man first if the train (i) is moving towards the man, (ii) is at rest, (iii) is moving away from the man?

7. A stream flows at u feet per second, and a man can row at c feet per second through the water. The width of the stream is x feet, and the man can row straight across

and back in the same time that he can row x_1 feet down-stream and back.   Prove that—

(i) $\dfrac{2x}{\sqrt{c^2-u^2}} = \dfrac{x_1}{c+u} + \dfrac{x_1}{c-u}.$

(ii) $x_1 = x\sqrt{\left(1 - \dfrac{u^2}{c^2}\right)}$

CHAPTER IV

CLOCKS

" Alice looked round in great surprise. ' Why, I do believe we've been under this tree all the time ! Everything's just as it was ! '

" ' Of course it is,' said the Queen ; ' what would you have it ? '

" ' Well, in *our* country,' said Alice, ' you'd generally get to somewhere else if you ran very fast for a long time, as we've been doing.'

" ' A slow sort of country ! ' said the Queen. ' Now *here*, you see, it takes all the running you can do to keep in the same place. If you want to get somewhere else, you must run at least twice as fast as that ! ' "—*Through the Looking-Glass*.

Observations at Different Places.

If several observers, who are recording the times of occurrence of a series of events, wish to exchange their results, it is necessary for them to compare their clocks. Preferably the clocks should be synchronised, but it would be sufficient to note the difference between each clock and some standard clock. The standard British clock registers what we call " Greenwich time."

Synchronising is a simple matter if the observers and their clocks are all at one place, but if the observation stations are far apart direct comparison is impossible, and we are forced to rely on indirect methods which may not be proof against criticism. To transport a clock from one station to another is not a reliable method, because the journey itself may set up an error in the running of the clock. The best method is to send signals from a standard station to all other stations, and use these signals to synchronise the various clocks or record their errors; this in fact is done each day by the radio signals sent out at noon from Greenwich. Radio signals travel with the velocity of light, and therefore, for such comparatively small distances as we are concerned with on the Earth, the time of transit of the signal is usually negligible. But for large distances, such as the distance of the Sun from the Earth, the time taken by the signal is material, and allowance must be made for it in setting the clock. We shall see, however, that the process involves another difficulty which we are powerless to remove. This is best illustrated by a numerical example. In order to avoid big numbers and to bring the arithmetic of this chapter into line with that of the last, we shall introduce (temporarily) a new unit of length :

$$60,000 \text{ km.} = 1 \text{ } leg.$$

The velocity of light is therefore 5 legs per second.

Synchronising Two Clocks.

Suppose that two observers A and C, relatively at rest to each other, are at a distance of 75 legs apart, as measured by their own rules ; this distance is about twelve times as much as the distance of the Moon from the Earth. We shall examine the process by which A and C attempt to synchronise their clocks.

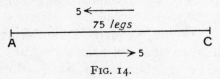

FIG. 14.

Since light travels at 5 legs per second, A and C calculate that a ray of light sent by either to the other will take $\frac{75}{5} = 15$ seconds to travel across the space separating them.

It is agreed that, at the instant when A's clock records zero hour, A shall send a light-signal to C, and that C, immediately he receives it, shall reflect it back to A.

C therefore *sets* his clock at 15 *seconds past zero*, but does *not start it* until the signal from A arrives. Immediately C receives the signal, he starts his clock and believes that it now agrees with A's clock. This opinion is shared by A, who, when he sees his clock indicating 15 seconds past zero, says to himself, "At this moment C is receiving my signal." From A's point of view, the fact appears to be established beyond doubt when the return signal from C reaches A at the instant his (A's) clock registers 30 seconds past zero. We know that A's receipt of the return reflected signal must occur at this instant, because otherwise A would be able to calculate his velocity through the ether (compare p. 32), and this, as we have seen, is impossible. In the same way, C, when he sees his clock indicating 30 seconds past zero, says to himself, "At this moment A is receiving the return signal," and this opinion is confirmed by the fact that, if A then reflects the signal back to C, it will reach C when C's clock indicates 45 seconds past zero, for the same reason as before.

Now there can be no ambiguity as regards the time indicated by C's clock of an event happening to C, nor as regards the time indicated by A's clock of an event happening to A. But we shall see that there is unfortunately a great deal of uncertainty as to the time indicated by A's clock of an event happening to C, or *vice versa*. If the clocks of A and C are genuinely synchronised, this uncertainty would not exist. But if there are grounds for suspecting that A and C are mistaken in their belief that they have succeeded in synchronising their clocks, there is no direct method of either of them ascertaining the time by his own clock of an event which is happening to the other. Although, when A sees that his clock reads 15 seconds past zero, he says that at this moment his signal is arriving at C, yet he has no direct method of making sure that this statement is true. And, by enlisting the evidence of an eye-witness, we shall show that there are different, but equally trustworthy, opinions of the time recorded by A's clock of the arrival of the signal at C.

An Onlooker's Opinion.

We now introduce an onlooker O, who considers that the world of A and C is moving away from him in the direction A→C at 4 legs per second.

Each individual acts on the supposition that he himself is at rest. In the following inquiry into O's opinions, we must therefore regard O as at rest and A, C as moving away from O. But if we had to inquire into the views of A or C, we should have to regard them as at rest and O as moving away from each of them in the opposite direction.

Suppose that A is passing O at the moment when A sends out his first light signal, and that O also sets his clock at zero at this instant. We can connect O with the world of A, C most easily by imagining that A combines his time-signal with a performance of the M.-M. experiment.

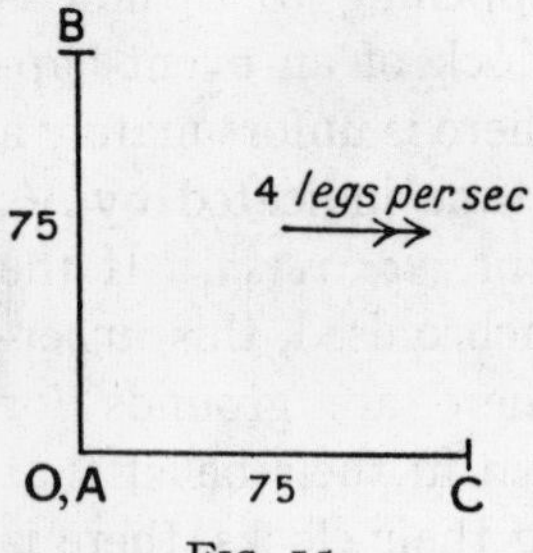

A marks out a track AB at right angles to AC and makes it 75 legs long by his rule, and places a mirror at B in the usual way. At the same time as he sends his light signal to C he sends another to B, and, as we know, both rays, reflected back, return to A at the same moment.

FIG. 15.

Now O and A agree that the length of AB is 75 legs, because for lengths across the stream their rules are identical. Also O, A, and C all agree that light travels at 5 legs per second through the ether.

Fig. 16 represents *O's idea* of the path pursued by the light signal, which is directed to the mirror at B.

By the time the light signal impinges on the mirror at B, the arm AB has moved to the position A_1B_1, so that the signal starts from O, A and impinges on the mirror at B_1, and therefore travels along OB_1; by the time it returns to

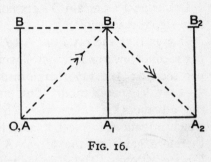

FIG. 16.

A the arm AB has moved to the position A_2B_2, so that the return path is B_1A_2.

The arm AB is advancing at 4 legs per second and the light signal travels along OB_1 at 5 legs per second. Suppose the outward journey takes t seconds. Then $OB_1 = 5t$ legs, $BB_1 = 4t$ legs, $OB = 75$ legs,

$$\therefore \text{ by Pythagoras, } (5t)^2 = (4t)^2 + 75^2.$$
$$\therefore 25t^2 - 16t^2 = 75^2 \text{ or } 9t^2 = 75^2 \text{ or } 3t = 75.$$

$$\therefore t = \frac{75}{3} = 25 \text{ seconds.}$$

∴ the total time out and back *according to O's clock* is
    $2 \times 25 = 50$ seconds.

But by the M.-M. experiment the ray returns to A from C at the same moment as the ray from B.

∴ *by O's clock*, the ray returns to A from C at 50 seconds past zero.

But *A's clock* registers 30 seconds past zero when the ray returns to A from C.

∴ the arrival of the ray back at A is said by O to occur at 50 seconds past zero by O's clock, and to occur at 30 seconds past zero by A's clock.

Therefore, although O's clock and A's clock agreed at zero hour, they do not agree afterwards: we may therefore say that the synchronisation between O and A has disappeared.

Let us next ascertain O's opinion as to the time when the first signal reached C.

O says that the ray from A to C is advancing at 5 legs per second towards a target C which is retreating at 4 legs per second: the ray therefore gains on the target C at 5−4=1 leg per second. But on the return journey the ray advances at 5 legs per second towards a target A which advances to meet it at 4 legs per second: the ray therefore gains on the target A at the rate of 5+4=9 legs per second. The distance which the ray has to gain on its target is the same on each journey (A and C believe this distance is 75 legs; O does not agree with them: but we need not stop to ascertain O's estimate of the distance), therefore the outward journey A→C takes 9 times as long as the journey back from C to A, so that $\frac{9}{10}$ths of the total time is spent on the outward journey, and $\frac{1}{10}$th of the total time on the return journey. Now the total time, out and back, by O's clock is 50 seconds.

∴ O says the outward journey, A→C, takes $\frac{9}{10}$th of 50
=45 seconds, and the journey back from C to A takes
$\frac{1}{10}$th of 50=5 seconds.

∴ *O says* that the ray arrives at C at 45 seconds past
zero *by O's clock*.

Also since A's clock records the total time, out and back, as 30 seconds, we see in the same way that *O says* that the ray arrives at C at $\frac{9}{10}$th of 30=27 seconds past zero by *A's clock*.

Further, when the ray arrives at C, we know that C's clock registers 15 seconds past zero and is set going at this instant.

The occurrence of the event consisting of the arrival of the ray at C is therefore *registered by O* as follows :

O's CLOCK.	A's CLOCK.	C's CLOCK.
45 seconds past zero.	27 seconds past zero.	15 seconds past zero.

This is O's opinion of the operation. A of course does not agree with O ; when A's clock registers 27 seconds past zero, A says that it is long past the time of C's receipt of the signal.

O, however, says that C's clock has been set 27—15 =12 second-spaces behind A's clock.

We can easily continue this process of calculating the times registered by O of further events. Consider the arrival of the ray back at A from C.

C dispatches the ray to A and receives it back again reflected from A after a total interval of $\dfrac{2 \times 75}{5}$=30 seconds, by C's clock.

Now O says that the time from C to A is only $\frac{1}{10}$th of the total time C→A and A→C.

Therefore O says that the ray takes $\frac{1}{10}$th of 30 =3 seconds, by C's clock, to travel from C to A. But the time on C's clock when the ray left C was 15 seconds past zero ; therefore the time on *C's clock* when the ray arrives at A is 15+3=18 seconds past zero, *according to O.*

The occurrence of the event consisting of the arrival of the ray back at A is therefore *registered by O* as follows :

O's CLOCK.	A's CLOCK.	C's CLOCK.
50 seconds past zero.	30 seconds past zero.	18 seconds past zero.

It is worth comparing these two events as *recorded by O*.

	O's Clock.	A's Clock.	C's Clock.
Event I. (arrival at C)	45	27	15 seconds past zero.
Event II. (return to A)	50	30	18 seconds past zero.
Time-interval between the events	5	3	3 seconds.

O therefore says that A's clock and C's clock run at the same rate (each registers the *interval* between the two events as 3 seconds), but both their clocks lose time (each records an interval as 3 seconds which is really 5 seconds long) and C's clock has been set 12 seconds behind A's clock.

What other Onlookers Think.

Now these calculations which O has made have depended on the fact that the world of A, C is moving away from O at 4 legs per second. Suppose that there is another onlooker P, who notes that the world of A, C is moving away from him in the direction A→C at (say) 3 legs per second. Then the same argument which has been used to obtain O's records may be used to obtain P's records of the various events, but the arithmetic will be different, and P's opinion about the behaviour of the clocks of A and C will not agree numerically with O's opinion. P will say that A and C have failed to synchronise, but will form a different estimate of the amount C's clock is behind A's clock, and will assess at a different figure the rate at which both A's clock and C's clock lose. It is left to the reader to make the necessary calculations, see Exercise IV., No. 2. Each onlooker, therefore, has his own standard of time ; and his judgment of the time-interval separating two events will differ from that formed by another observer moving relatively to him. This agrees with what has been said in the previous chapter. But the example we have just taken shows also that it is impossible to synchronise two clocks which are situated at different places. For, although the inhabitants of the world in which the clocks are at rest believe that they have secured synchronisation, the observers in other worlds not only deny that they have done so, but disagree amongst themselves as to the amount of the difference between the clocks. No setting of the clocks can therefore ever secure general approval, or indeed approval by the inhabitants of more than one world.

Simultaneous Events.

If after A and C believe they have synchronised their clocks, an event takes place at A and another event takes place at C, and if each records the time of the event which has happened to himself, and if these two records are the same, then A and C will say that the two events happened simultaneously. But with the data of our example, we see that O will say that the event at A took place before the event at C, for according to O when A's clock reads 27 seconds past zero C's clock reads 15 seconds past zero. Therefore if A and C both say that the times of the events are 27 seconds past zero, O says that, when the event occurs at A, C's clock has only got as far as 15 seconds past zero and therefore the event at C, timed as 27 seconds past zero at C, has not yet occurred. In fact the time-interval between these two events is $27-15=12$ seconds as measured by the clock-rate of A or C, which is equivalent to 20 seconds as measured by the clock-rate of O, for 5 of O's seconds are the same as 3 of A's seconds or C's seconds. O will therefore say that the event at A took place 20 seconds (by O's clock) before the event at C.

A and C therefore call two events simultaneous which

O considers occur at a definite time-interval, and other onlookers will agree with O in saying that the events are not simultaneous, but will disagree with O as to the length of the time-interval between them. It is therefore impossible to attach any meaning to a general statement that two events at different places occurred at the same time. If the time-standard of one world makes them simultaneous, the time-standard of other worlds require a time-interval between the events. Since there is no reason to prefer the opinion of one onlooker to that of any other, we cannot say that any one opinion is more correct than any other. The bare statement that two events at different places were simultaneous is, therefore, devoid of meaning, unless we also specify the world in which this time-measure has been made.

Union of Space and Time.

Time by itself ceases to be an absolute idea; it is a property of the world in which it is measured, and each world has its own standard.

Each individual has, of course, his own time-rule and his own distance-rule which he thinks of as absolute, because he thinks of his own world as at rest. But in a sense this is a delusion, because a transference to another world will modify each of them; a change in time-measure is bound up with a change in distance-measure. As we have already seen, the onlookers do not agree with A, C, or each other as to the distance between the two places where the events occurred, any more than they agree with the time-interval between the events. To quote the celebrated phrase of *Minkowski*: "From now onwards space and time sink to the position of mere shadows, and only a sort of union of both can claim an independent or absolute existence"—*i.e.* an existence to which all onlookers will give equal recognition and apply equal standards of measurement. We shall see later what form this union takes.

EXERCISE IV

1. A and C measure their distance apart as 50 legs ; an on-looker P notes that the world of A, C is moving away from him in the direction A→C at 3 legs per second. A passes P at zero hour by A's clock and P's clock, at which moment A sends a light signal to C in order to synchronise with C ; this signal is reflected back to A. What is P's estimate of the times recorded on the three clocks of (i) the arrival of the signal at C, and (ii) the return of the signal to A ?

2. Repeat No. 1, if A and C are 75 legs apart.

3. With the data of No. 1, D is a person in the world of A and C at a distance of 100 legs from A and on the other side of A from C. If A and D synchronise, find the difference between their clocks according to P in terms of second-spaces (i) on A's clock, (ii) on P's clock.

4. Repeat No. 1, assuming that the world of A, C is moving away from P in the direction C→A at 3 legs per second, P and A being as before at the same place at zero hour.

5. With the data of No. 1, if an Event I. occurs at A and an Event II. occurs at C, and if A and C describe these events as simultaneous as recorded by their own clocks, which event will P consider to have occurred first ? Repeat this problem with the data of No. 4.

6. Two events, I., II., occur simultaneously at different places in the world of A and C. An onlooker O says that I. occurred before II. Would it ever be possible for some other onlooker to say that II. occurred before I. ?

7. With the data of No. 1, find P's estimate of the distance of A from C.

CHAPTER V

ALGEBRAIC RELATIONS BETWEEN TWO WORLDS

"The progress of Science consists in observing inter-connections and in showing with a patient ingenuity that the events of this ever-shifting world are but examples of a few general relations, called laws. To see what is general in what is particular, and what is permanent in what is transitory, is the aim of scientific thought."—A. N. WHITEHEAD, *An Introduction to Mathematics*.

Generalisations.

We have shown in the previous chapters, by means of numerical examples, that any eye-witness will consider that standards of measurement of distance and time vary from one world to another. The real nature of these variations cannot be appreciated unless we pass on from numerical illustrations to general formulæ. We therefore shall now proceed to express in algebraic form the relations between two worlds which are moving with *uniform* velocity relatively one to another. These formulæ may then be utilised for solving special numerical cases.

It will simplify the work if we introduce a new unit of length :

$$300,000 \text{ km. } (i.e. \text{ 5 legs}) = 1 \text{ } lux.$$

The velocity of light is therefore 1 lux per second.

Statement of the Problem.

It may assist the reader if we state in great detail the problem proposed for solution in this chapter.

The world of A and C is moving away from O in the direction A→C at a uniform velocity of u luxes per second ; at the instant when A passes O, both A and O set their clocks at zero hour. A and C are at rest relatively to each other, and they measure their distance apart as x_1 luxes. A and C believe they have synchronised their clocks.

An event (Event I.) occurs at A at zero hour by A's clock ; another event (Event II.) occurs at C at t_1 seconds past zero by C's clock. Therefore in the world of A and C the *distance-interval* between the two events is x_1 luxes, and the *time-interval* between the two events is t_1 seconds. There is complete agreement between A and C as to both of these interval measurements. Each regards both himself and the other as at rest in the ether. Their distance-measures agree because they can use the same rule to measure out AC ; their time-measures agree, because otherwise they could deduce the velocity of their common world through the ether.

Next consider O's point of view. He says that Event I. occurs at O at zero hour, and that Event II. occurs at C at (say) t seconds past zero by his own (O's) clock. O regards himself as at rest and A, C as moving away from him. O therefore takes the distance-interval between the two events as the distance of C from him at the moment when Event II. takes place. Suppose that O's measure of this distance is x luxes. Then O *says* that the distance-interval between the two events is x luxes and the time-interval between the two events is t seconds.

In short, the interval between the two events is registered by A or C as x_1 luxes, t_1 seconds, and by O as x luxes, t seconds.

What are the formulæ which connect x, t with x_1, t_1 ?

Before tackling this general problem, we shall ascertain O's opinion about the measuring-rule used by A or C, the running of their clocks, and their attempts to synchronise.

Measuring-Rules.

A marks out a length AC of x_1 luxes along the line of motion of A's world relatively to O. What is the length of AC, according to O ?

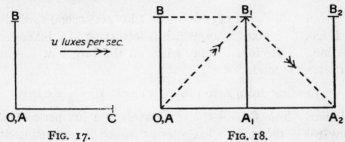

FIG. 17.   FIG. 18.

Suppose that O is watching A performing the M.-M. experiment. A and C agree that the lengths of AC and AB are each x_1 luxes, O agrees that the length of AB is x_1 luxes, but says that the length of AC is different, say z luxes.

O says that the arm AB moves away from him at u luxes per second, so that the ray sent towards the mirror at B impinges on it when AB has moved into the position A_1B_1; the path of the ray is therefore AB_1. Similarly, the ray returns to A when AB has moved into the position A_2B_2, so that the return path is B_1A_2.

Suppose the time from A to B_1 or from B_1 to A_2, is k seconds by O's clock. O makes the following calculations :

$AB_1 = k$ luxes (light travels along AB_1 at 1 lux per second).

$BB_1 = ku$ luxes (AB advances at u luxes per second).

$AB = x_1$ luxes (O agrees with A's measurements across the stream).

$$\therefore \text{ by Pythagoras, } k^2 = k^2u^2 + x_1^2$$
$$\therefore k^2 - k^2u^2 = x_1^2 \text{ or } k^2(1 - u^2) = x_1^2$$
$$\therefore k^2 = \frac{x_1^2}{1 - u^2}.$$

The total time by O's clock from A to B and back is $2k$ seconds.

∴ the total time by O's clock from A to C and back is
$$2k \text{ seconds.}$$

But O can also reason as follows :

From A to C, the ray travels at 1 lux per second towards a target C, z luxes away, which is retreating at u luxes per second. Therefore the ray gains on the target at $(1-u)$ luxes per second.

∴ the time from A to C by O's clock is $\dfrac{z}{1-u}$ seconds.

Similarly from C to A the ray travels at 1 lux per second towards a target A, z luxes away, which is advancing at u luxes per second. Therefore the ray gains on the target at $(1+u)$ luxes per second.

∴ the time from C to A by O's clock is $\dfrac{z}{1+u}$ seconds

∴ the total time from A to C and back is $\dfrac{z}{1-u}+\dfrac{z}{1+u}$ seconds

$$=\frac{z(1+u)+z(1-u)}{(1-u)(1+u)}=\frac{z+zu+z-zu}{1-u^2}=\frac{2z}{1-u^2} \text{ seconds.}$$

But the total time by O's clock is $2k$ seconds.

$$\therefore \frac{2z}{1-u^2}=2k \text{ or } z=k(1-u^2)$$

$$\therefore z^2=k^2(1-u^2)^2, \text{ but } k^2=\frac{x_1{}^2}{1-u^2}$$

$$\therefore z^2=\frac{x_1{}^2}{1-u^2}(1-u^2)^2=x_1{}^2(1-u^2)$$

$$\therefore z=x_1\sqrt{(1-u^2)}.$$

Therefore *O says* that a length in the direction of motion which A and C measure as x_1 luxes is really $x_1\sqrt{(1-u^2)}$ luxes :

Or, in proportion, what A and C measure as 1 lux is in O's opinion really $\sqrt{(1-u^2)}$ luxes.

Now $\sqrt{(1-u^2)}$ must be less than 1; consequently O *says* that the measuring-rule used by A and C, when placed along the line of motion, *contracts*; and the contraction-ratio is $\sqrt{(1-u^2)}$.

Comparison by O of A's Clock and C's Clock with O's Clock.

Our numerical examples have shown that every one will agree that A's clock runs at the same rate as C's clock. The reason for this may be stated as follows:

An essential feature in every argument is that each individual regards himself as at rest in the ether and that all the observations he makes must bear this out. He cannot make any measurement which will reveal his velocity through the ether. A and C agree that their distance apart is x_1 luxes: they therefore argue that a time signal sent from either to the other and reflected back will return after $2x_1$ seconds, and their clocks must bear this out. But the experiment in which A sends a signal to C and receives it back again is identical with the experiment in which C sends a signal to A and receives it back again. Both A's clock and C's clock record the time of this experiment as performed by each of them as $2x_1$ seconds. Therefore A's clock and C's clock must run at the same rate. We have seen from numerical examples that O admits this, but says that both clocks lose and that they have not been synchronised. Let us now calculate O's estimate of the time-difference between A's clock and C's clock.

In order to synchronise the clocks, A proposes at zero hour by his clock to send a light-ray to C. As they agree that AC is x_1 luxes, they calculate that the signal will take x_1 seconds to reach C. Consequently C sets his clock at x_1 seconds past zero and starts it at the instant the light-ray arrives.

Now we have just seen that by O's clock the time from A to C is $\dfrac{z}{1-u}$ seconds, and the total time out and back is $\dfrac{2z}{1-u^2}$ seconds. O therefore says that the fraction of the total time out and back occupied by the journey out is

$$\frac{z}{1-u} \div \frac{2z}{1-u^2} = \frac{z}{1-u} \times \frac{(1+u)(1-u)}{2z} = \frac{1+u}{2}.$$

Now A's clock registers $2x_1$ seconds for the total time out and back. Therefore O says that, when the ray arrives at C, A's clock registers $\dfrac{1+u}{2} \times 2x_1 = x_1(1+u)$ seconds past zero. But at this instant C's clock starts off at x_1 seconds past zero.

∴ A's clock is ahead of C's clock by $x_1(1+u) - x_1$ seconds
$$= x_1 + x_1 u - x_1 = x_1 u \text{ seconds.}$$

Therefore when A and C think they have synchronised their clocks, O says that A's clock is $x_1 u$ second-spaces ahead of C's clock.

The difference between the clocks depends on the value of x_1, the length of AC. Therefore the farther C is away from A in the direction of motion of the world of A, C from O, the more A's clock is ahead of C's clock, according to O. Suppose, for example, the world of A, C is moving due east away from O. Then A's clock is ahead of any clock east of A and is behind any clock west of A. Both these results are expressed in the statement given above, because, if C is west of A, x_1 is negative, and a clock which is a negative number of seconds ahead of another clock is, of course, a positive number of seconds behind it.

We must therefore regard each place on the line of motion of AC as having its own clock: the inhabitants of the world of A, C think all these clocks are synchronised, but O says each registers a local time whose difference from that of A is given by the formula above. We may express the facts by a diagram showing the local time, according to O, of the instant when A is passing O,

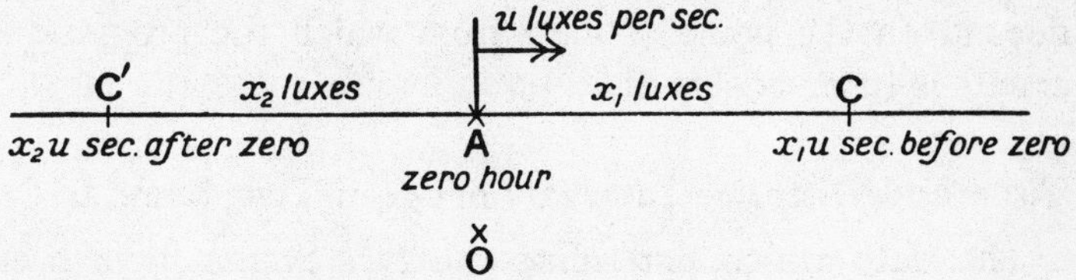

FIG. 19.

which is taken as zero hour both by A and O. The distances indicated in the diagram represent A's or C's measurements.

Clock-Rates.

A and C record the time-interval between two events as 1 second. What is O's estimate of this time-interval by his own clock?

With our previous notation, we know that O says that the time from A to C and back is $2k$ seconds by O's clock, where $k^2 = \dfrac{x_1^2}{1-u^2}$ or $k = \dfrac{x_1}{\sqrt{(1-u^2)}}$.

But A says that the time from A to C and back is $2x_1$ seconds by A's clock and O must agree with him.

∴ O says that $2x_1$ seconds on A's clock measures the same time-interval as $2k$ seconds $= \dfrac{2x_1}{\sqrt{(1-u^2)}}$ seconds on O's clock.

∴ O says that (in proportion) 1 second on A's clock measures the same time-interval as $\dfrac{1}{\sqrt{(1-u^2)}}$ seconds on O's clock.

It is important to remember that this is a statement of *O's view* about the behaviour of A's clock.

Since $\sqrt{(1-u^2)}$ is less than 1, $\dfrac{1}{\sqrt{(1-u^2)}}$ is greater than 1, and therefore O says that A's clock loses. But, of course, A equally says that O's clock loses. Our results always depend on the point of view from which the progress of events is being observed.

Time and Distance Intervals between Two Events.

The data which determine the two events have been stated in great detail on p. 54. The diagram represents *O's view* of the events.

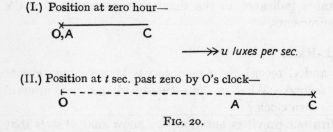

(I.) Position at zero hour—

O,A   C

———⟫ *u luxes per sec.*

(II.) Position at *t* sec. past zero by O's clock—

O   A   C

FIG. 20.

Event I. occurs at zero hour at A at the instant when A is passing O. Event II. occurs at C at t seconds past zero by O's clock. A and C say that the distance-interval between the two events is x_1 luxes, *i.e.* their measure of AC is x_1 luxes. O says that Event I. occurred at O, and that Event II. occurred at the position of C at t seconds past zero by O's clock. O therefore says that the distance-interval between the two events is x luxes, which is his measure of the length of OC in (II.). O also says that the measure of OA in (II.) is ut luxes, because A is moving away from him at u luxes per second.

∴ O says that by his rule AC$=x-ut$ luxes.

Now A measures AC as x_1 luxes and O says that a measurement of 1 lux by A is really $\sqrt{(1-u^2)}$ luxes (see

p. 56). Therefore O says that AC is really $x_1\sqrt{(1-u^2)}$ luxes.

$$\therefore x_1\sqrt{(1-u^2)}=x-ut$$

$$\therefore x_1=\frac{x-ut}{\sqrt{(1-u^2)}}.$$

This relation is very important.

Again, suppose that the time of Event II. at C is recorded by C's clock as t_1 seconds past zero. Then A and C must agree that the time-interval between the events is t_1 seconds.

Now O says that A's clock is x_1u seconds ahead of C's clock (see p. 58). Therefore O says that, when Event II. occurs, the time on A's clock is t_1+x_1u seconds past zero. But we know that 1 second on A's clock measures the same time-interval as $\dfrac{1}{\sqrt{(1-u^2)}}$ seconds on O's clock.

$\therefore$ when Event II. occurs, the time on O's clock is $\dfrac{t_1+x_1u}{\sqrt{(1-u^2)}}$ seconds past zero ; but the time on O's clock is t seconds past zero.

$$\therefore t=\frac{t_1+x_1u}{\sqrt{(1-u^2)}}$$

$$\therefore t_1+x_1u=t\sqrt{(1-u^2)} ; \text{ now } x_1=\frac{x-ut}{\sqrt{(1-u^2)}}$$

$$\therefore t_1=t\sqrt{(1-u^2)}-\frac{u(x-ut)}{\sqrt{(1-u^2)}}=\frac{t(1-u^2)-u(x-ut)}{\sqrt{(1-u^2)}}$$

$$=\frac{t-u^2t-ux+u^2t}{\sqrt{(1-u^2)}}$$

$$\therefore t_1=\frac{t-ux}{\sqrt{(1-u^2)}}.$$

This relation is also of great importance. It may be a help to the reader if we re-state what has been established.

Two events occur at distance-interval x_1 luxes and time-interval t_1 seconds according to A, C, and at distance-interval

x luxes and time-interval t seconds according to O. The world of A, C is moving away from the world of O at u luxes per second, and distances are measured as positive in the direction of motion of A from O. Then A's records are connected with O's records by the formulæ :

$$x_1 = \frac{x - ut}{\sqrt{(1 - u^2)}}; \ t_1 = \frac{t - ux}{\sqrt{(1 - u^2)}}.$$

If then we know the distance interval and the time-interval between two events as recorded in one world, we can calculate the distance and time-intervals between these two events as recorded in any other world moving with uniform velocity relative to the former, along the line joining the two events.

A's Opinion of O's Records.

It has been pointed out frequently in previous chapters that there is no observer whose records are entitled to more respect than those of any other observer. It is therefore essential to show that the formulæ just obtained are consistent with this view. Using the same notation and axes as before, A says that O is moving away from him at $(-u)$ luxes per second. Now A says that the distance and time-intervals between the events are x_1 luxes and t_1 seconds.

∴ the formulæ just obtained show that

O's distance-interval should $= \dfrac{x_1 - (-u)t_1}{\sqrt{(1 - u^2)}} = \dfrac{x_1 + ut_1}{\sqrt{(1 - u^2)}}$

and O's time-interval should $= \dfrac{t_1 - (-u)x_1}{\sqrt{(1 - u^2)}} = \dfrac{t_1 + ux_1}{\sqrt{(1 - u^2)}}$

∴ the formulæ just obtained should be equivalent to

$$x = \frac{x_1 + ut_1}{\sqrt{(1 - u^2)}} \text{ and } t = \frac{t_1 + ux_1}{\sqrt{(1 - u^2)}}.$$

Unless they are, there is not that reciprocal relation

between O and A which the Theory of Relativity requires. We may state the problem as follows :

Given that $x_1 = \dfrac{x-ut}{\sqrt{(1-u^2)}}$ *and* $t_1 = \dfrac{t-ux}{\sqrt{(1-u^2)}}$

Prove that $x = \dfrac{x_1+ut_1}{\sqrt{(1-u^2)}}$ *and* $t = \dfrac{t_1+ux_1}{\sqrt{(1-u^2)}}.$

(i) We have $x_1 + ut_1 = \dfrac{x-ut}{\sqrt{(1-u^2)}} + \dfrac{u(t-ux)}{\sqrt{(1-u^2)}}$

$$= \frac{x-ut+ut-u^2x}{\sqrt{(1-u^2)}} = \frac{x(1-u^2)}{\sqrt{(1-u^2)}}$$

$$= x\sqrt{(1-u^2)}$$

$$\therefore \; x = \frac{x_1+ut_1}{\sqrt{(1-u^2)}}.$$

(ii) We have $t_1 + ux_1 = \dfrac{t-ux}{\sqrt{(1-u^2)}} + \dfrac{u(x-ut)}{\sqrt{(1-u^2)}}$

$$= \frac{t-ux+ux-u^2t}{\sqrt{(1-u^2)}} = \frac{t(1-u^2)}{\sqrt{(1-u^2)}}$$

$$= t\sqrt{(1-u^2)}$$

$$\therefore \; t = \frac{t_1+ux_1}{\sqrt{(1-u^2)}}.$$

We therefore see that the relations which express A's opinion of O's world are consistent with, and can be deduced from, the relations which express O's opinion of A's world.

The Velocity of Light.

The formulæ which connect the two worlds introduce the expression $\sqrt{(1-u^2)}$, which is imaginary if $u>1$, *i.e.* if the velocity of one world relatively to the other is greater than the velocity of light. We therefore say that we can have no experience of a body moving with a velocity greater than that of light. And in all our results u must stand for a fraction between $+1$ and -1. It is customary to represent $\sqrt{(1-u^2)}$ by $\dfrac{1}{\beta}$ or to put $\beta = \dfrac{1}{\sqrt{(1-u^2)}}$ so that $\beta > 1$. In this case, the standard formulæ may be written :

$$x_1 = \beta(x-ut) \; ; \; t_1 = \beta(t-ux)$$

or

$$x = \beta(x_1+ut_1) \; ; \; t = \beta(t_1+ux_1)$$

$$\text{where } \beta = \dfrac{1}{\sqrt{(1-u^2)}} > 1.$$

And the results on pp. 59–60 may be stated as follows :

(i) O says that the length of a line in the direction of motion which A measures as 1 lux is $\dfrac{1}{\beta}$ luxes.

(ii) O says that a time-interval which A's clock records as 1 second is β seconds.

EXERCISE V

1. The world of A is moving at $\frac{3}{5}$ lux per second due east from O. What is O's opinion about (i) the length of A's foot-rule, (ii) the rate of running of A's clock ? What is A's opinion about O's foot-rule and O's clock ?

2. A and C, who are relatively at rest at a distance apart of 5 luxes, have synchronised their clocks ; the world of A, C is moving away from O in the direction A→C at $\frac{7}{25}$ lux per second. A passes O at zero hour by O's clock and A's clock. What does O say is the difference between A's clock and C's clock ? D is a place in the world of A, C, such that $DA = 10$ luxes, $DC = 15$ luxes. What does O say is the difference between D's clock and A's clock ? What does O say is the time recorded by the clocks of A, C, D when O's clock records 25 seconds past zero ?

3. With the data of No. 1, A records two events as happening at an interval of 5 seconds and at a distance apart of 3 luxes, the second event being due east of the first event. What are the time and distance-intervals of the events as recorded by O ?

4. With the data of No. 3, solve the question if the second event is due west of the first event.

5. Given that $x_1 = \dfrac{x - ut}{\sqrt{1 - u^2}}$ and $x = \dfrac{x_1 + ut_1}{\sqrt{1 - u^2}}$

   Prove that $t_1 = \dfrac{t - ux}{\sqrt{1 - u^2}}$ and $t = \dfrac{t_1 + ux_1}{\sqrt{1 - u^2}}$.

6. If Event I. is the dispatch of a light-signal by A and Event II. is the receipt of the light-signal by C, show that with the usual notation (i) $x_1 = t_1$, (ii) $x = t$. What does this mean in terms of O's opinion?

7. Using the equations on p. 63, prove that $x^2 - t^2$ is always equal to $x_1^2 - t_1^2$.

CHAPTER VI

THE SEPARATION OF EVENTS

" ' That's the effect of living backwards,' the Queen said
kindly ; ' it always makes one a little giddy at first, but there's
one great advantage in it, that one's memory works both
ways.'

" ' I'm sure *mine* only works one way,' Alice remarked.
' I can't remember things before they happen.'

" ' It's a poor sort of memory that only works backwards,'
replied the Queen."—*Through the Looking-Glass.*

THE position of an event in history is fixed if we know
(i) when, and (ii) where it took place. These necessary data
must be expressed with reference, at any rate implicitly,
to some standard event. The " when " is usually referred
to the Christian Era, t years A.D. ; the " where," if
on the Earth's surface, may be described in terms of
longitude and latitude, the standard being the Greenwich
meridian and the Equator. Astronomers often state
the " where " of an event in space in terms of Right
Ascension and Declination, together with some distance
measurement.

Any event is, therefore, fixed by recording its time-
interval and its space-interval from some actual or hypothetical standard event. Now we have seen that both
these records vary with the world in which they are observed.
To say that the battles of Waterloo and Hastings occurred
at an interval of 749 years is an intelligible statement if
addressed to people on this Earth. It would convey no

meaning, or in fact a false one, to some one in a world moving rapidly along the line joining Hastings and Waterloo. If these two events had been recorded in this other world, the time-interval (and the space-interval) would be quite different. It is obviously desirable to try to discover some property connecting the two events whose measure will have the same numerical value, in whatever world records of the events are made. If this can be done, we can regard such a property as something absolute, independent of all observers, retaining the same value however it is viewed. Measures of time-intervals and distance-intervals are not absolute in this sense : they vary from world to world. But there is a kind of union of the two about which opinions do not change, a union which will be measured with equal magnitudes by all observers. We shall first consider a numerical example to show what the nature of this union is.

Records of the Interval between Two Events by Various Observers.

A's world observes two special events and notes that Event II. occurs 12 seconds later than Event I. and at a distance 4 luxes due east of it. The points at which Events I., II. occur will be called E, F respectively.

A writes his record of the interval between the events in the form (4 ; 12). With our previous notation, this is short for $x_1=4$; $t_1=12$.

(i) O is an observer who says that A's world is moving away from him at $\frac{3}{5}$ lux per second due east. How does O record the interval between the events ?

We have the relations

$$x = \frac{x_1 + ut_1}{\sqrt{(1 - u^2)}} ; \quad t = \frac{t_1 + ux_1}{\sqrt{(1 - u^2)}}$$

where $(x ; t)$ is O's record and $x_1=4$, $t_1=12$, $u=\frac{3}{5}$.

$$\sqrt{(1-u^2)} = \sqrt{(1-\tfrac{9}{25})} = \sqrt{(\tfrac{16}{25})} = \tfrac{4}{5}$$

$$\therefore \; x = \frac{4+\tfrac{3}{5}\times 12}{\tfrac{4}{5}} = \frac{20+36}{4} = \frac{56}{4} = 14$$

$$\text{and } t = \frac{12+\tfrac{3}{5}\times 4}{\tfrac{4}{5}} = \frac{60+12}{4} = \frac{72}{4} = 18$$

$\therefore$ O records the interval between the events as 14 luxes and 18 seconds, or, more shortly, (14 ; 18).

(ii) P is an observer who says that A's world is moving away from him at $\tfrac{3}{5}$ lux per second due west. How does P record the interval between the events ?

Using the same formulæ as before, we now have

$$x_1 = 4, \; t_1 = 12, \; u = -\tfrac{3}{5}$$
$$\therefore \; \sqrt{(1-u^2)} = \sqrt{(1-\tfrac{9}{25})} = \sqrt{(\tfrac{16}{25})} = \tfrac{4}{5}$$
$$\therefore \; x = \frac{4+(-\tfrac{3}{5})12}{\tfrac{4}{5}} = \frac{20-36}{4} = -\frac{16}{4} = -4$$
$$\text{and } t = \frac{12+(-\tfrac{3}{5})4}{\tfrac{4}{5}} = \frac{60-12}{4} = \frac{48}{4} = 12$$

$\therefore$ P records the interval as -4 luxes and 12 seconds, or, more shortly, $(-4 ; 12)$.

This means that P says Event II. occurs 4 luxes west of Event I.

(iii) Q is an observer who says that A's world is moving away from him at $\tfrac{4}{5}$ lux per second due east. What are Q's records ?

Here $x_1 = 4, \; t_1 = 12, \; u = \tfrac{4}{5}$
$$\therefore \; \sqrt{(1-u^2)} = \sqrt{(1-\tfrac{16}{25})} = \sqrt{(\tfrac{9}{25})} = \tfrac{3}{5}$$
$$\therefore \; x = \frac{4+(\tfrac{4}{5})12}{\tfrac{3}{5}} = \frac{20+48}{3} = \frac{68}{3}$$
$$\text{and } t = \frac{12+(\tfrac{4}{5})4}{\tfrac{3}{5}} = \frac{60+16}{3} = \frac{76}{3}$$

$\therefore$ Q records the interval as

$$\frac{68}{3} \text{ luxes, } \frac{76}{3} \text{ seconds, or } \left(\frac{68}{3} ; \frac{76}{3}\right).$$

We will set down the records of three other observers, leaving the calculations to the reader.

(iv) R is an observer for whom $u=-\frac{4}{5}$.

Show that R's record is $\left(-\dfrac{28}{3};\dfrac{44}{3}\right)$.

(v) S is an observer for whom $u=\frac{12}{13}$.

Show that S's record is $\left(\dfrac{196}{5};\dfrac{204}{5}\right)$.

(vi) T is an observer for whom $u=-\frac{7}{25}$.

Show that T's record is $\left(\dfrac{2}{3};\dfrac{34}{3}\right)$.

Let us now collect these results in a single table, arranging them so that the distance-intervals are in ascending order of magnitude, apart from sign.

A.	OBSERVER.	T.	P.	R.	O.	Q.	S.
—	Value of u luxes per second	$-\frac{7}{25}$	$-\frac{3}{5}$	$-\frac{4}{5}$	$\frac{3}{5}$	$\frac{4}{5}$	$\frac{12}{13}$
4	Distance-interval, x luxes .	$\frac{2}{3}$	-4	$-9\frac{1}{3}$	14	$22\frac{2}{3}$	$39\frac{1}{5}$
12	Time-interval, t seconds .	$11\frac{1}{3}$	12	$14\frac{2}{3}$	18	$25\frac{1}{3}$	$40\frac{4}{5}$

This table shows that if in passing from one world to another the distance-interval (apart from sign) is increased, then the time-interval is also increased.

What relation connects the values of t and x? A glance at the table does not suggest any obvious relation. But if we write down corresponding values of t^2 and x^2, it is not difficult to guess the answer. This is done below :

Thus for R we have $t=14\frac{2}{3}$, $x=-9\frac{1}{3}$;

$$\text{therefore } t^2=(14\tfrac{2}{3})^2=\frac{44}{3}\times\frac{44}{3}=\frac{1936}{9}=215\tfrac{1}{9},$$

$$\text{and } x^2=(-9\tfrac{1}{3})^2=\frac{28}{3}\times\frac{28}{3}=\frac{784}{9}=87\tfrac{1}{9}.$$

	A.	T.	P.	R.	O.	Q.	S.
t^2	144	$128\frac{4}{9}$	144	$215\frac{1}{9}$	324	$641\frac{7}{9}$	$1664\frac{14}{25}$
x^2	16	$\frac{4}{9}$	16	$87\frac{1}{9}$	196	$513\frac{7}{9}$	$1536\frac{14}{25}$
$t^2 - x^2$	128	128	128	128	128	128	128

In each case, we see that $t^2 - x^2 = 128$.

Although the time-interval t seconds and the distance-interval x luxes varies from one world to another, all observers alike agree that the value of $t^2 - x^2$ is 128.

We shall represent the expression $t^2 - x^2$ by s^2, so that in the special case above we have $s^2 = 128$ or $s = \sqrt{(128)} = 11\cdot3$, as measured by every observer: and we say that $11\cdot3$ measures the *separation* of the two events. This name is due to *Professor Whitehead*.

The separation of two events defined by the formula

$$s^2 = t^2 - x^2$$

is an entirely new conception; it is neither time nor distance, but some kind of fusion of the two. Its importance arises from the fact that it is independent of the world in which the records are made; all observers attribute to it the same numerical measure, provided it is agreed to measure time in seconds and distance in luxes. The separation, therefore, represents something absolute, some intrinsic property connecting the two events, without regard to the conditions under which the events are observed.

Formal Treatment of Separation.

If, with our previous notation, A records the interval between two events as x_1 luxes, t_1 seconds, and if O records the interval between the same events as x luxes, t seconds, then we can prove that $t^2 - x^2 = t_1^2 - x_1^2$.

Using the formulæ $x = \dfrac{x_1 + ut_1}{\sqrt{(1-u^2)}}$; $t = \dfrac{t_1 + ux_1}{\sqrt{(1-u^2)}}$

we have $t^2 - x^2 = \dfrac{(t_1 + ux_1)^2}{1-u^2} - \dfrac{(x_1 + ut_1)^2}{1-u^2}$

$$= \frac{(t_1{}^2 + 2ut_1x_1 + u^2x_1{}^2) - (x_1{}^2 + 2ut_1x_1 + u^2t_1{}^2)}{1-u^2}$$

$$= \frac{t_1{}^2 + 2ut_1x_1 + u^2x_1{}^2 - x_1{}^2 - 2ut_1x_1 - u^2t_1{}^2}{1-u^2}$$

$$= \frac{t_1{}^2(1-u^2) - x_1{}^2(1-u^2)}{1-u^2}$$

$$= t_1{}^2 - x_1{}^2.$$

If then we represent $t^2 - x^2$ by s^2, we see that $t_1{}^2 - x_1{}^2$ also equals s^2, and therefore the value of s as calculated by one observer is the same as the value of s calculated by any other observer. Consequently the separation between two events, as defined above, survives transformation from one world to another. An expression of this kind is called an *invariant*. Its measure has nothing to do with the circumstances of the observer; it represents an objective relation between, or a physical property of, the events themselves.

Real and Imaginary Values of the Separation.

In the numerical example discussed above (p. 68), the value of $t^2 - x^2$ was positive, and therefore the value of s, its square root, was real. But if t is less than x, then $s^2 = t^2 - x^2 = $ a negative number ; in this case s is the square root of a negative number (as for example $\sqrt{-10}$) and is therefore imaginary. This does not of course mean the events are imaginary, but merely that the measure of the property, called the separation of the events, is expressed in some cases by an imaginary number. It is easy to see when this will happen.

Suppose Event I. occurs at E and Event II. occurs at F, and that the interval is x luxes, t seconds. Then a ray of light will take x seconds to move from E to F. Suppose now the time-interval between Events I. and II. is less than the time a light-ray takes to travel from E to F, then t is less than x and therefore $s^2 = t^2 - x^2 =$ a negative number. Therefore the separation is imaginary if the time-interval between the events is less than the time required to send a light signal from one place to the other : in other words, if the separation is imaginary it is impossible for a message, sent off from the place E where Event I. has occurred, describing that event, to arrive at the place F where Event II. occurs before the actual occurrence of Event II. This fact will be recognised by all observers alike, for if one observer obtains an imaginary value for the separation, so will they all.

If, however, s is real, t is greater than x. Consequently, if as soon as Event I. has occurred at E a wireless signal reporting the event is dispatched to F, every one will agree that it will reach F before Event II. occurs.

The intermediate case when s is zero is easy to interpret. This requires that $t = x$ or that the time-interval between the events is equal to the time a light-signal takes to travel from the one place to the other. Suppose that Event I. is the dispatch of a light-signal from E, and that Event II. is the receipt of this light-signal at F, then $t = x$ and the separation is zero. The Sun is 93,000,000 miles, or 500 luxes, away from the Earth. If Event I. occurs on the Sun and if Event II. occurs after a time-interval of 8 minutes 20 seconds ($=$500 seconds) on the Earth, then the separation between these two events is zero.

It is important to remember that when an observer puts on record the time of an event, he does not give the time at which he *sees* the event take place, but the *corrected* time after allowing for the time the light-ray has taken to reach him—*i.e.* he records the actual time at which he believes the event took place, not the time at which he saw it happen. For example, the observed time of an eclipse of one of Jupiter's moons would depend on how far away Jupiter was from the Earth when the eclipse was observed. To find the time at which the eclipse really happened, allowance must be made for the time the light-ray took to reach the Earth. It was the discrepancy between the calculated times and the observed times of the eclipses of Jupiter's moons which first enabled a Danish astronomer, *Roemer*, in 1675, to calculate the velocity of light.

Time-Order of Two Events.

Suppose that O records the interval between Event I. at E and Event II. at F as x luxes, t seconds, where x and t are each positive, so that Event II. occurs *after* Event I. and distances in the direction E to F are measured as positive. Suppose another observer A is moving relatively to O in the direction E to F at u luxes per second, so that u is also positive. A records the time-interval as t_1 seconds. Then we know that

$$t_1 = \frac{t - ux}{\sqrt{(1 - u^2)}}.$$

If t_1 is positive, A says that Event II. occurs after Event I. ; but if t_1 is negative, A says that Event II. occurs *before* Event I.

Is it conceivable that, after all proper corrections (as noted above) have been made, O and A should disagree as to the order in which the events took place ? The answer is bound up with the nature of the separation between the events.

(i) An Imaginary Separation.

If the separation is imaginary, t^2 is less than x^2, and therefore, as each is positive, t is less than x.

Put $t = vx$ so that $v < 1$.

We then have $t_1 = \dfrac{t-ux}{\surd(1-u^2)} = \dfrac{vx-ux}{\surd(1-u^2)} = \dfrac{x(v-u)}{\surd(1-u^2)}$.

Now u can never be greater than 1 ; no observer can move faster than a light ray. But u can have any value between 0 and 1, because we can think of A as moving away from O with any velocity up to 1 lux per second.

∴ since $v<1$, we can think of an observer A who is moving away from O with a velocity greater than v luxes per second, *i.e.* so that $u>v$.

But if $u>v$, $v-u$ is negative

∴ t_1 is negative

∴ this observer A says that Event II. occurs *before* Event I.

Again, since $v<1$, we can choose an observer B who is moving away from O with a velocity exactly equal to v luxes per second, *i.e.* so that $u=v$.

But if $u=v$, $v-u=0$

∴ $t_1=0$

∴ this observer B says that Event II. occurs *simultaneously* with Event I.

Again, we can obviously choose an observer C who is moving away from O with a velocity less than v luxes per second, *i.e.* so that $u<v$; then $v-u$ is positive

∴ t_1 is positive

∴ this observer C agrees with O that Event II. occurs *after* Event I.

Now all these observers are equally entitled to their own views. Their time-records are of course *actual* as opposed to *observed* times—that is to say, the observer takes the time of his clock when he sees the event happen, and corrects for the time the light-ray has taken to reach him. In this way he obtains what he calls the actual time at which the event took place. But as no preference can be given to any one observer over any other, we are forced to conclude that *it is meaningless to attach a time-order to events whose separation is imaginary*. For such events we may say, using comparative terms, that whereas in slow-moving worlds Event II. occurs *after* Event I., in fast-moving worlds Event II. occurs *before* Event I., and there is one world in which the Events are actually simultaneous. Another descriptive form of this statement is based on the idea that the occurrence of any event cannot be said to be caused by any event which follows it. If some observers say that Event I. occurs before Event II., while other observers with equal justice say that Event II. occurs before Event I., then it is impossible to imagine that there is any causal relation between the events. Now this is what happens when t is less than x, *i.e.* when the time-interval between the events is less than the time a light-ray takes to travel from one place to the other. If, then, we substitute for " causal relation " the word " force," and if we say that neither event can exert a force on the other event, we are really saying that no force can be propagated with a velocity greater than that of light. If, for example, the Sun is regarded as exerting a gravitational force on the Earth, the propagation of this force takes at least 500 seconds to reach the Earth from the Sun. We shall, however, see later that Einstein's theory abolishes the idea of a gravitational force altogether.

(ii) A Real Separation.

If the separation is real, t^2 is greater than x^2, and therefore t is greater than x.

Put $t = vx$ so that $v > 1$.

Then, as before, $t_1 = \dfrac{x(v-u)}{\sqrt{(1-u^2)}}$.

Now u can never be greater than 1, but v is greater than 1;

$$\therefore v > u$$
$$\therefore t_1 \text{ is always positive.}$$

Every observer will therefore agree with O that Event II. occurs *after* Event I.

Consequently, if the separation is real, the time-order of the two events is definite, the same for every one.

We know that different observers make different time-sections of the Universe : but all observers alike will place Event I. in a time-section which precedes their time-section containing Event II. For each of them, Event I. appears as a feature in the story leading up to Event II., and may therefore be said to contribute, however indirectly, to the occurrence of Event II. We may say that when the separation is real there is some causal connection between the events.

Proper Time.

Suppose with our previous notation A records two events which happen to him. He says the time-interval is t_1 seconds, and the distance-interval is zero, for both events occur at the same place, namely, the place where he is. The separation between the events is given by $s^2 = t_1^2 - 0^2 = t_1^2$ or $s = t_1$.

Now consider an observer O who says that A's world is moving away from him at u luxes per second : suppose as usual that Event I. occurs at zero hour when A is passing O. Then O records the interval between the events as x luxes, t seconds. The following diagram exhibits the two views :

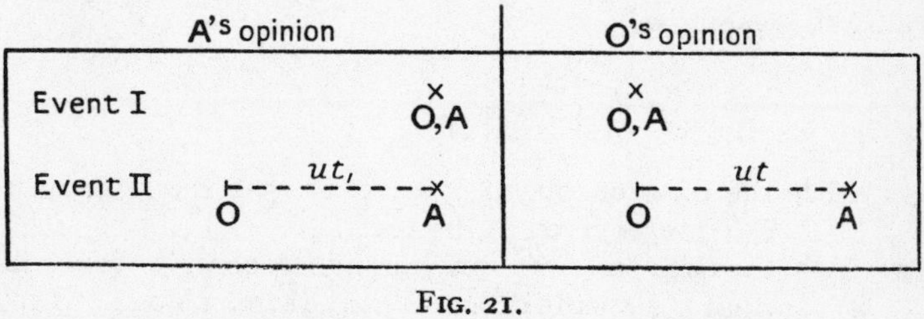

A's opinion	O's opinion
Event I × O,A	× O,A
Event II ⊢――― ut_1 ―― × O A	⊢――― ut ――― × O A

FIG. 21.

Since both events happen to A, O says that the distance-interval x luxes equals ut luxes ; $x = ut$.

O also says the separation is given by $s^2 = t^2 - x^2$

$$\therefore t_1^2 = s^2 = t^2 - x^2 = t^2 - u^2 t^2 = t^2(1 - u^2)$$
$$\therefore t_1 = t\sqrt{(1 - u^2)}.$$

Now t_1 seconds is the time-interval recorded by A, the person to whom the events happen. It is the time according to which each individual records the incidents of his own life, and it is called the " Proper Time " for the individual concerned. Since $\sqrt{(1 - u^2)}$ is less than 1, we see that t_1 is less than t, and consequently the proper time between two events is less than the time-interval recorded by any other observer. If we consider the life-history of an individual, the measure of the time-interval between two events will depend on the observer ; but if we regard the individual as carrying his own clock about with him, we call his measure of the time-interval the " proper time," and it is less than that of any one else. He is in fact measuring the separation between two events wholly in time, while other observers measure it partly in time and partly in distance. An observer whose measure takes more distance must also automatically take more time as well, in compensation. The separation between two events is equal to the proper time between them, that is, the time-interval as measured by the person to whom the events happen. Of course if the separation is imaginary it is impossible for the two events to happen to the same person, and " proper time " ceases to exist.

EXERCISE VI

1. With the data on pp. 68, 70, verify that the records of R, S, T are as given in the text.
2. With the data on p. 68, can you find an observer who will say that the events occurred at the same place ? If so,

what velocity does this observer attribute to A, and what is his measure of the time-interval ?

3. A gives the interval between two events in the form $x_1 = 3$, $t_1 = 5$. O says that for A's world $u = \frac{5}{13}$. What are O's records for the interval ? What is the separation ?

4. A records the interval between two events as 5 luxes, 13 seconds; O records the time-interval as 15 seconds. What is O's record of the distance-interval ? What is the separation ? What velocity does O attribute to A ?

5. O says that Event I. at E is given by $t = 2$, $x = 5$, and Event II. at F is given by $t' = 6$, $x' = 12$; units being seconds and luxes. What are the time- and distance-intervals as recorded by O ? If A is moving away from O in the direction E to F at $\frac{3}{5}$ lux per second, what is the time-interval according to A ? Interpret your result. What is the separation ?

6. O says that two events happen at different places at the same time. What can you say about their separation and their time-order ?

7. O says that two events happen at different times at the same place. What can you say about their separation and their time-order ?

8. With the data of No. 5, can you find an observer for whom the events will be simultaneous ?

9. On the same day the following events are noted :

    Event   I. Earthquake at Tokio at 12 noon.

    Event II. Formation of a Sun-spot at 12·06 p.m.

    Event III. Disappearance of the Sun-spot at 12.12 p.m.

What can you say about the time-order of these events ?

10. I get out of bed at 7 a.m. and retire to bed at 10 p.m., Greenwich time; an observer says that my bed has moved 72,000 luxes in the interval. How long does he say I have been out of bed? If a man at Greenwich says that I have moved about with the velocity of light all the time I have been out of bed, how long do I say the time is?

CHAPTER VII

THE FOURTH DIMENSION

" There is no difference between Time and any of the three dimensions of space except that our consciousness moves along it. . . . The civilised man can go up against gravitation in a balloon ; why should he not hope that ultimately he may be able to stop or accelerate his drift along the Time dimension, or even turn about and travel the other way ? "—H. G. WELLS, *The Time Machine.*

HITHERTO we have only considered events which occur at points in a straight line along which the worlds are separating. It is easy to extend what has been said so as to include events occurring at any points in space.

Points in a Plane.

If we take two perpendicular lines in the plane, we can fix the position of any point in the plane by stating its distances from these two lines. For example, take a point O and draw from it a line Ox due east and a line Oy due north. Suppose any point A

FIG. 22.

is 5 miles east and 3 miles north of O ; this fixes the position of A. If we start at O and walk 5 miles x-wards, *i.e.* eastwards to M, and then walk 3 miles y-wards, *i.e.* northwards along MA, we arrive at A. The distances 5 and 3 are called the co-ordinates of A ; we say that the point A is given by $x=5$, $y=3$, or that its co-ordinates are (5, 3).

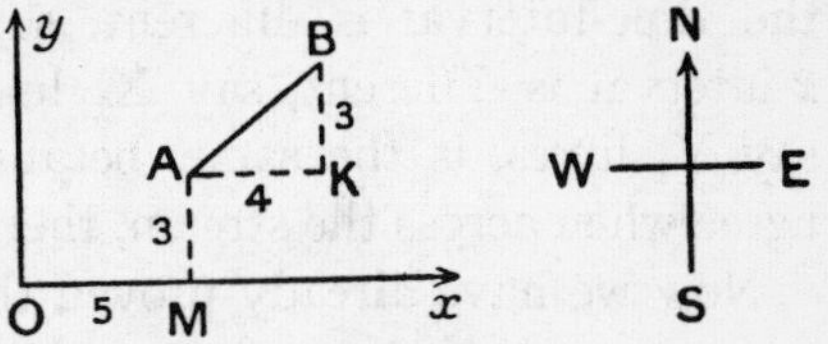

The x-co-ordinate is always put first. Suppose that B is another point in the plane and that its co-ordinates are $(9, 6)$, then we can move from A to B by going a farther distance $9-5=4$ miles x-wards and $6-3=3$ miles y-wards. In the figure, $AK=4$, $KB=3$

$$\therefore AB^2=AK^2+BK^2=4^2+3^2.$$

In the same way, if the distance-interval between A and B is X units x-wards and Y units y-wards, so that $AK=X$ and $BK=Y$, we have

$$AB^2=X^2+Y^2.$$

The co-ordinates of a point are simply its distance-intervals from O measured (i) x-wards, (ii) y-wards. If we know the co-ordinates of any two points A and B, we can find the distance-intervals of B from A measured x-wards and y-wards by subtracting the x-co-ordinates and the y-co-ordinates, as above.

Suppose now an observer O says that the world of A, B is moving away from him in the direction Ox at u luxes per second, and that an Event (I.) occurs at A and another Event (II.) occurs at B after an interval T seconds. Then O says that the interval between the events is T seconds, X luxes x-wards, Y luxes y-wards. Now in the world of A, the time-interval is different, say T_1 seconds; and the x-interval is different, say X_1 luxes; but the y-interval, say Y_1 luxes, is the same, because the rules of O and A agree when across the stream, therefore $Y=Y_1$.

Now we have already proved that $T^2-X^2=T_1^2-X_1^2$

$$\therefore \text{ since } Y=Y_1, \ T^2-X^2-Y^2=T_1^2-X_1^2-Y_1^2.$$

But if O measures the length of AB as r luxes and A measures the length of AB as r_1 luxes, we know that

$$X^2+Y^2=r^2 \text{ and } X_1^2+Y_1^2=r_1^2.$$
$$\therefore T^2-r^2=T_1^2-r_1^2.$$

We therefore put $s^2=T^2-X^2-Y^2=T^2-r^2$, and call s the *separation* between the events whose intervals are

(X, Y ; T) according to O and $(X_1, Y_1 ; T_1)$ according to A, and whose space-intervals are r, r_1 according to O, A.

Points in Space. |

To fix the position of any point in space, we take three mutually perpendicular planes, called the planes of reference, and measure the distance of the point from each plane.

Suppose, for example, we draw on a horizontal plane a line Ox due east, a line Oy due south, and a line Oz vertically upwards. A point A in the air could be fixed by saying it was 4 miles east of O, 3 miles south of O, and at a height of 2 miles above O. If we start at O and walk 4 miles x-wards, *i.e.* eastwards to P, and then walk 3 miles y-wards, *i.e.* southwards along PM to M, and then rise 2 miles z-wards, *i.e.* vertically upwards along MA, we arrive at A. The distances 3, 4, 2 are called the co-ordinates of A ; we say that the point A is given by $x=4$, $y=3$, $z=2$, or that its co-ordinates are (4, 3, 2). The co-ordinates are always written in this order, x, y, z.

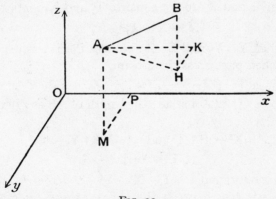

FIG. 23.

Now suppose we move from A to any point B by travelling X units x-wards along AK to K, and then Y units

y-wards along KH to H, and then Z units z-wards along HB to B. We say that the distance-intervals of B from A are X, Y, Z.

Now $\angle$AKH is a right angle,

$$\therefore AH^2 = AK^2 + KH^2 = X^2 + Y^2.$$

Also $\angle$AHB is a right angle,

$$\therefore AB^2 = AH^2 + HB^2 = X^2 + Y^2 + Z^2.$$

This shows how the length of AB can be calculated as soon as we know the distance-intervals of B from A, and as before we can calculate these, by subtraction, if we know the co-ordinates of A and B.

Suppose now an observer O says that the world of A, B is moving away from him in the direction Ox at u luxes per second, and that an event (I.) occurs at A and another event (II.) occurs at B after an interval T seconds.

Then O says that the interval between the events is T seconds, X luxes x-wards, Y luxes y-wards, Z luxes z-wards. Suppose A says that these intervals are respectively T_1 seconds, X_1, Y_1, Z_1 luxes. Then we know that although T and X are not equal to T_1 and X_1, yet

$$T^2 - X^2 = T_1^2 - X_1^2.$$

Further, $Y = Y_1$ and $Z = Z_1$, because the rules of A and O agree when put across the stream.

$$\therefore T^2 - X^2 - Y^2 - Z^2 = T_1^2 - X_1^2 - Y_1^2 - Z_1^2.$$

Suppose O and A measure the length of AB as r luxes and r_1 luxes respectively.

Then $r^2 = X^2 + Y^2 + Z^2$ and $r_1^2 = X_1^2 + Y_1^2 + Z_1^2$

$$\therefore T^2 - r^2 = T_1^2 - r_1^2.$$

We therefore put $s^2 = T^2 - X^2 - Y^2 - Z^2 = T^2 - r^2$, and call s the *separation* between the events whose intervals are (X, Y, Z ; T) according to O and $(X_1, Y_1, Z_1 ; T_1)$ according to A, and whose space-intervals are r, r_1 according to O, A.

We have now applied the idea of *separation* to any two

events occurring at any points of space and time, and have thereby constructed a function or expression which may properly be called a physical reality.

Four-Dimensional Space-Time.

In order to specify the time and space-intervals between two events, we see that it is necessary to give values to four different variables, each of which can change independently of the others, namely X, Y, Z, T.

Although each observer distinguishes sharply between space and time, the distinction drawn by one observer is not the same as that drawn by another. What one measures as " time," another measures partly in space and partly in time. The distinction, therefore, between space and time is subjective—that is to say, the observer, although unconsciously, is affected by his circumstances in his discrimination between the two. We cannot therefore suppose that this distinction corresponds to an objective physical reality. And so we are forced to the conclusion that we live in a four-dimensional world, divided arbitrarily by each observer into three dimensions of space and one dimension of time, but in reality an entity to be called *space-time*.

Owing to the fact that people on the Earth never move relatively to each other with really high velocities, the time and distance axes of any one person agree fairly well with those of any other. Life would be a perplexing and embarrassing matter if this agreement did not exist. But the distinction between space and time drawn by an inhabitant of a Beta particle moving with a velocity approaching that of light is so widely different from that of the physicist observing him that any kind of common social life would be unthinkable.

Every observer maps out the Universe with his own space and time axes. Suppose an observer A were to classify a large number of events all of which occurred at the same moment. Then this collection of events forms a time-section or time-cleavage by A of the Universe. Now events which are simultaneous for A are usually not simultaneous for O. Suppose O takes one event in A's list and proceeds to make a catalogue of events simultaneous with it. Then we know that O's list will not agree with A's list : in other words, O's time-cleavage of the Universe is not the same as A's ; they may have some members in common, but speaking in general terms there will be far more disagreement than agreement.

The Universe is to be regarded as a collection of events, anywhere and anywhen, an entity which mathematicians call a *continuum*, and the difference between O and A is simply that they slice it up differently. The Universe as an entity is time-less (and space-less). What each individual perceives is merely his own time-section. History records some of the time-sections of our ancestors, and Mr. H. G. Wells forecasts time-sections of our descendants. With neither group have we the power to obtain direct acquaintance, merely because we cannot put ourselves into the position in which the desired time-cleavage would be the natural one. But all events, past, present, and future as we call them, are present in our four-dimensional space-time continuum, a universe without past or present, as static as a pile of films which can be formed into a reel for the cinematograph. It is obviously absurd to attempt to form a picture of a four-dimensional Universe, but it may suggest ideas if we consider the structure of a three-dimensional Universe whose inhabitants partition it by two axes of space and one axis of time.

Flat-Land.

Suppose a worm can crawl anywhere on a vast horizontal plane surface, but has no power of raising itself out of the

plane or burrowing into it ; and, better still, imagine that
the worm has no idea that there is even such a thing as
" above " or " below." In that case the worm is living in
a three-dimensional con-
tinuum, two dimensions
in space and one dimen-
sion in time, forming his
space-time world.

Draw two perpen-
dicular straight lines *ox*,
oy on the plane, and draw
a line *ot* perpendicular to
the plane to represent the
time-axis. The worm, of
course, cannot picture this
line *ot* any more than we

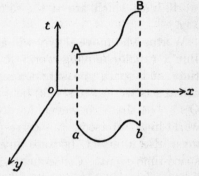

FIG. 24.

can visualise a fourth axis of reference in addition to three
mutually perpendicular axes chosen for our space-axes.

Suppose the worm starts its life at the point *a*, co-
ordinates x_1, y_1, at a time an observer O at rest at *o* records
as t_1 seconds past zero. Then O denotes this event by the
point A in space whose co-ordinates are x_1, y_1, t_1. As the
worm moves about on the plane, each event in its life is
represented by a point in space. Finally, the worm dies
at *b*, co-ordinates x_2, y_2, at a time O records as t_2 seconds
past zero. Then O represents this event, the worm's
death, by the point B in space, co-ordinates x_2, y_2, t_2. The
whole history of the worm from birth to death is then
represented by a curve in space starting at A and ending
at B. And we say, using *Minkowski's* phrase, that the
curve AB is the " *world-line* " of the worm. Suppose now
that there are numerous worms and other objects in the
plane. Each has its own world-line, and if we take the
complete collection of all these world-lines, they constitute
the space-time worm Universe. The collision of any two

objects, in fact the happening of any event, is recorded by an intersection of two world-lines. If O compiles a catalogue of simultaneous events, he is simply making a time-section of these world-lines, and is choosing points on the world-lines which are at the same height above the plane *xoy*.

Worms who move slowly will agree with O's conclusions. But a rapidly moving worm R will make such different time and space measurements that the world-lines he constructs will (so to speak) be quite a different shape from O's. The shape, however, hardly matters. If two of O's world-lines intersect, the corresponding world-lines of R must also intersect, because any intersection represents a space-time event. Consequently, if we think of O's world-lines as forming a vast network in space, then R's world-lines will also form a network. The meshes in the one system may be quite different in size and shape from those in the other; but to each mesh and each corner of that mesh of O's network there will correspond a unique mesh and a unique corner of that mesh of R's network.

Straight World-Lines.

World-lines can clearly be of any shape; given the observer, the shape is an index of the worm's history. What meaning must be attributed to the statement that a world-line is straight?

Choose the origin O so that the worm is born at O at zero hour and dies at P, co-ordinates X_1, Y_1 at T_1 seconds past zero according to the observer O. Draw PC parallel to the time-axis and of length T_1 units; draw PM perpendicular to Ox so that $OM=X_1$, $MP=Y_1$.

Then O and C represent in space-time the birth and death of the worm. Suppose the worm's world-line is the straight line OC. Let K, any point on OC, represent an event in the life of the worm, and suppose the co-ordinates of K are X, Y, T; in our figure, ON=X, NQ=Y, QK=T.

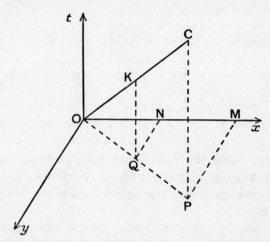

Fig. 25.

Our co-ordinates measure the distance and time-*intervals* since the birth of the worm.

From similar triangles, $\dfrac{KQ}{CP} = \dfrac{OQ}{OP} = \dfrac{QN}{PM} = \dfrac{ON}{OM}$

$\therefore \dfrac{T}{T_1} = \dfrac{OQ}{OP} = \dfrac{Y}{Y_1} = \dfrac{X}{X_1}.$

This means that the time-intervals and the space-intervals, measured from the birth of the worm, all increase at the same uniform rate; and it also follows that the separation of an event from O increases at the same uniform rate.

The observer, therefore, says that a worm, whose world-line is straight, is moving with uniform speed in a straight line: on the Newtonian Theory, the worm would be moving freely, uninfluenced by any force.

A numerical example may help to make these ideas more intelligible.

Let us suppose that the progress of the worm is represented by the following table, the units of time and space being seconds and luxes :

Event.	A.	B.	C.	D.	E.	F.	G.	H.	K.
Time T . . .	0	13	26	39	52	65	78	91	104
x-co-ordinate X .	0	3	6	9	12	15	18	21	24
y-co-ordinate Y .	0	4	8	12	16	20	24	28	32

In this table the space- and time-intervals measured from the start all increase at the same uniform rate.

Take, for example, the interval between the events D and E ;

$$T = 52 - 39 = 13 ; \quad X = 12 - 9 = 3 ; \quad Y = 16 - 12 = 4$$

$\therefore$ the space-interval of E from $D = \sqrt{(X^2 + Y^2)} = \sqrt{(9 + 16)}$

$$= \sqrt{25} = 5$$

the separation of E from $D = \sqrt{(T^2 - X^2 - Y^2)} = \sqrt{(169 - 25)}$

$$= \sqrt{144} = 12.$$

We should obtain the same numerical results for any other pair of successive events.

Further, the space-interval of K from A is the sum of the space-intervals A to B, B to C, C to D, . . . H to K ; and the separation of K from A is the sum of the separations B from A, C from B, D from C, . . . K from H. For the space-interval of each portion is 5, and therefore the sum of the eight space-intervals is $8 \times 5 = 40$; while the space of interval of K from A is

$$\sqrt{24^2 + 32^2} = \sqrt{576 + 1024} = \sqrt{1600} = 40.$$

Similarly, the separation of each portion is 12, and therefore the sum of the separation for the eight intervals is $12 \times 8 = 96$; while the separation of K from A is

$$\sqrt{104^2 - 24^2 - 32^2} = \sqrt{10816 - 1600} = \sqrt{9216} = 96.$$

Curved World-Lines.

The fact that if a line is *straight*, the distance of the end-point from the starting-point is equal to the sum of the lengths of the various portions of the line is a fundamental fact in ordinary geometry. We have now seen that, correspondingly, if a world-line is straight the separation of the last event from the first event is equal to the sum of the separations between successive events measured along the line.

If a line is *curved*, the distance of the end-point from the starting-point is *less* than the sum of the lengths of the various portions of the curved line. In contrast to this, we shall show that if a world-line is *curved*, the separation of the last event from the first event is *greater* than the sum of the separations between successive events measured along the world-line.

A world-line is associated with the history of an actual particle; it represents the movement of the particle as viewed by some observer. The speed of the particle cannot, therefore, exceed the velocity of light. If the interval between any two events in the history of the particle is measured by T seconds, R luxes, we know that $T > R$ and therefore the separation is real. In the numerical example, given above, if $T=13$ we have $R=5$.

Now consider a worm whose world-line consists of two straight portions AB and BC. Suppose the events A, B, C are recorded by O as follows :

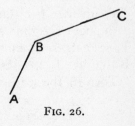

A, $t=0$, $x=0$, $y=0$;
B, $t=13$, $x=2$, $y=5$;
C, $t=26$, $x=6$, $y=8$;

Fig. 26.

the units being seconds and luxes.

Then the intervals are

A to B, $T_1=13$, $X_1=2$, $Y_1=5$

B to C, $T_2=26-13=13$, $X_2=6-2=4$, $Y_2=8-5=3$

$$\therefore \frac{T_1}{T_2}=1,\ \frac{X_1}{X_2}=\frac{2}{4}=\frac{1}{2},\ \frac{Y_1}{Y_2}=\frac{5}{3}.$$

∴ the co-ordinates do not increase at equal rates, and so the world-line ABC is not straight.

The separation of B from A is

$$\sqrt{(13^2-2^2-5^2)}=\sqrt{(169-4-25)}=\sqrt{(140)}.$$

The separation of C from B is

$$\sqrt{(13^2-4^2-3^2)}=\sqrt{(169-16-9)}=\sqrt{(144)}=12.$$

The separation of C from A is

$$\sqrt{(26^2-6^2-8^2)}=\sqrt{(676-36-64)}=\sqrt{(576)}=24.$$

But $\sqrt{(140)}$ is less than 12

∴ the separation of B from A+the separation of C from B is *less* than the separation of C from A.

We see, then, in this case that if the world-line ABC is not straight, the separation of C from A is greater than what we may call the separation *measured along the world-line* ABC.

We shall now give a general proof of this result.

Straight and Curved World-Lines.

If the world-line ABC of a particle is straight, we know that it moves with uniform velocity in a straight line. This involves two things :

Suppose the time and space-intervals from A to B are T_1 seconds, r_1 luxes, and the corresponding intervals from B to C are T_2 seconds, r_2 luxes.

Then (i) the space-interval of C from A is r_1+r_2 luxes.

(ii) $\dfrac{r_1}{T_1}=\dfrac{r_2}{T_2}$, for these fractions represent the *speed* of the body from A to B and from B to C.

It is, of course, true that the time-interval of C from A is T_1+T_2 seconds, but this is true whether the world-line is straight or curved, if we are dealing with the progress of a body.

Now if either of the conditions (i) and (ii) ceases to be true, the world-line is no longer straight ; the portion AB will no longer be in the same straight line with BC.

Condition (i) holds only if the *space-movement* of the body is a straight line ; condition (ii) holds only if the body moves at a constant speed. Each condition is necessary for *uniform velocity*. Thus if the body describes a straight line at variable speed, (i) holds and (ii) fails, and if the body describes (say) two sides of a triangle in the plane with constant speed, (i) fails and (ii) holds. In each case the world-line is not straight. Of course if the body moves in a plane curve with variable speed, both conditions fail.

Separation measured along a World-Line.

If the world-line AB of a body is straight, with the above notation, we know that the separation of B from A is $\sqrt{(T_1{}^2-R_1{}^2)}$. We can represent this geometrically by drawing a right-angled triangle abH, so that $ab=T_1$, aH$=R_1$, and $\angle a$H$b=90°$.

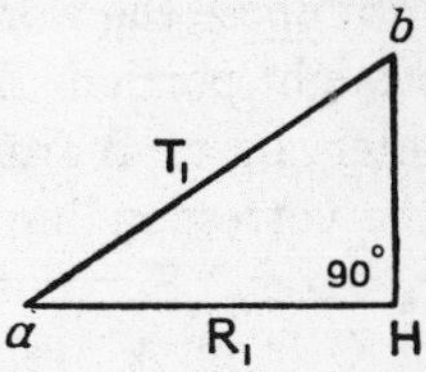

Then by Pythagoras, bH$^2+R_1{}^2=T_1{}^2$, or bH$^2=T_1{}^2-R_1{}^2$,

$$\therefore b\text{H}=\sqrt{(T_1{}^2-R_1{}^2)}.$$

Fig. 27.

The side bH therefore measures the separation.

Now suppose the world-line AC of a body is curved. Take a large number of successive events in the life of the body, D, E, F, G, . . . N. If we take a sufficient number, each portion AD, DE, EF, . . . of the world-line is nearly straight, and we can then find the separation, as above,

for each of these portions. If we add together all the
separations for the small portions, we say that the sum
is *the separation of C from A measured along the world-line*.

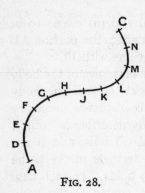

FIG. 28.

We shall prove that this is less
than the separation of C from A.
To do this, it will be sufficient to
show that if AB and BC are two
different straight world-lines, then
the separation of C from B+the
separation of B from A is less
than the separation of C from
A. For we can then argue as
follows :

The separation CA is greater than
the sum of the separations CD, DA;

which is greater than the sum of the separations CE, ED,
DA;

which is greater than the sum of the separations CF, FE,
ED, DA; and so on.

Maximum Separation.

Suppose the world-line of a body consists of two different
straight portions AB, BC, and suppose the time and space-
intervals of B from A are T_1 seconds, r_1 luxes, and that
the corresponding intervals of C from B are T_2 seconds,
r_2 luxes. Suppose also that the corresponding intervals
of C from A are T seconds, r luxes. Then $T = T_1 + T_2$;
and r cannot be greater than $r_1 + r_2$. Since AB is not in
a straight line with BC, we know that either $\frac{r_1}{T_1}$ is unequal
to $\frac{r_2}{T_2}$ or that $r_1 + r_2$ is greater than r. Possibly both these
conditions hold, but at least one must be true.

We shall represent the separations of B from A and
C from B by the method shown above.

Draw triangles aHb, bKC with bK parallel to aH, and so that $aH=r_1$, $ab=T_1$, $\angle aHb=90°$

and $bK=r_2$, $bc=T_2$, $\angle bKc=90°$.

Produce cK and aH to cut at N, then $bKNH$ is a rectangle.

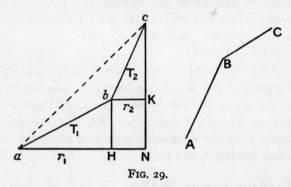

FIG. 29.

The separations of C from B and B from A are represented
by cK and bH, but $bH=KN$

∴ the separation of C from B+the separation of B from A
$=cK+bH=cK+KN=cN$.

Now the separation of C from A $=\sqrt{[T^2-r^2]}$

$$=\sqrt{[(T_1+T_2)^2-r^2]}$$

Now if $\dfrac{r_1}{T_1}$ is not equal to $\dfrac{r_2}{T_2}$, abH and bcK are triangles of
different shapes, so that the angles baH, cbK are unequal:
consequently ab is not in line with bc

∴ $ab+bc$ is greater than ac or $T_1+T_2>ac$.

Also r cannot be greater than r_1+r_2 and $r_1+r_2=aH+bK$
$$=aH+HN=aN$$

∴ the separation of C from A $=\sqrt{[(T_1+T_2)^2-r^2]}$
$$>\sqrt{[ac^2-(r_1+r_2)^2]} \text{ or } \sqrt{[ac^2-aN^2]}$$
$$>cN \text{ since } ac^2=aN^2+Nc^2$$
$$>\text{separation of C from B+separation of B}$$
$$\text{from A.}$$

But if $\frac{r_1}{T_1}$ should equal $\frac{r_2}{T_2}$, so that ab is in line with bc, then r_1+r_2 must be greater than r.

Now if ab is in line with bc, $ac=ab+bc=T_1+T_2$

$\therefore$ the separation of C from A

$= \surd[(T_1+T_2)^2-r^2] = \surd[ac^2-r^2]$

$> \surd[ac^2-(r_1+r_2)^2]$ or $\surd[ac^2-aN^2]$

$> cN$ as before

$>$ separation of C from B $+$ separation of B from A.

Consequently, if a world-line from A to C is not straight, the separation of C from A measured along the world-line is less than the direct separation of C from A—that is to say, is less than the separation measured along the *straight* world-line joining A and C.

The Geodesic Law of Motion.

Newton's first Law of Motion states that the progress of a body under the action of no forces is represented by a straight world-line. We can now state this law in more general terms.

If a body is moving freely, and if A and C are two events in its history, the space-time path followed by the body between A and C is such that the separation of C from A measured along that path is a maximum.

The striking feature of this statement is that it specifies a path which is unique, and is independent of the axes of reference or what is the same thing of the observers. There are an unlimited number of paths joining two points in space-time, but there is one of these which stands apart from all the rest in virtue of the fact that all observers alike agree that it yields a separation greater than the separation obtained by measurement along any other path. The world-line which has this unique property is called a *geodesic*.

It is interesting to note that if the body were to follow

a curved line from A to C travelling at the same speed as a light-ray, the separation along each portion of the curve would be zero, since $T=r$ for a light-ray, and therefore the total separation measured along this curved world-line would also be zero. We can, in fact, unite C with A by a curved world-line along which the separation can have any assigned value from the maximum down to zero, but the geodesic path is the only possible path for a body moving freely.

The only objective property we have so far discovered is this property called " separation." Time and space by themselves merely express relations between the observer and the thing observed : separation is the physical reality. Now in the previous chapter we saw that the separation between two events in the life of a body is equal to the " proper time " for that body—that is, the time-interval measured by a clock which the body carries about. We may therefore express the conclusions of this chapter by saying that bodies in the Universe, if left to themselves, follow the path which makes the proper time between their birth and death as great as possible. A body chooses the path which gives (in its own view) greatest length of life. If A and B represent any two events in the life of the body, the path from A to B is so chosen that its passage occupies the maximum amount of time (according to its own clock).

This rule of conduct has been called by Mr. Bertrand Russell the " Law of Cosmic Laziness " ; it is the substitute Relativity has made for the inclination of a body to follow " the line of least resistance."

EXERCISE VII

1. An event A is given by $x=1$, $y=3$, $z=8$, $t=35$, and an event B is given by $x=4$, $y=7$, $z=20$, $t=120$, units being luxes and seconds. What is the separation of B from A ?

2. With the data of No. 1, the world-line of a particle is the straight line AB. What are the space co-ordinates of an event happening to the particle when $t = 52$? What are the co-ordinates of the event happening to the particle for $z = 14$?

3. With the data of No. 1, another observer says that the events A and B both occur at the same place. What time-interval does he attribute to the two events ? What is the nature of a straight world-line joining A and B, as judged by this observer, and how is his time-reckoning described ?

4. What is the general appearance of the world-lines of (i) Trafalgar Square Tube Station, (ii) a train on the Bakerloo Tube, as observed by (a) a porter on the platform, (b) the engine-driver, (c) a person in the Sun.

5. The position of a particle in space-time is given by $x = 27a$, $y = 36a$, $z = 60a$, $t = 85a$, and the history of the particle is obtained by giving a successively all values from 0 to 4. What can you say about its world-line ? What is the separation between the events corresponding to $a = 4$ and $a = 0$?

6. Three events A, B, C in the life of a particle which moves in a plane are given by $t = 0$, $x = 0$, $y = 0$; $t = 17$, $x = 6$, $y = 15$; $t = 34$, $x = 18$, $y = 24$. What is (i) the separation of C from A, (ii) the sum of the separations of C from B and B from A. Is the particle moving freely ?

CHAPTER VIII

MASS AND MOMENTUM

"We recognise certain varying states or conditions of matter, and give one state one name and another another as though it were a man or a dog. Of matter in its ultimate essence and apart from motion we know nothing whatever. As far as we are concerned, there is no such thing."—SAMUEL BUTLER, *Notebooks*.

Composition of Velocity.

Suppose that in the world of A, B a body C starts from A at zero hour (both by A's clock and O's clock) and moves at a uniform rate to B, and according to A travels the distance AB=x_1 luxes in t_1 seconds. Suppose A measures the velocity of C as v luxes per second.

FIG. 30.

Then $v=\dfrac{x_1}{t_1}$.

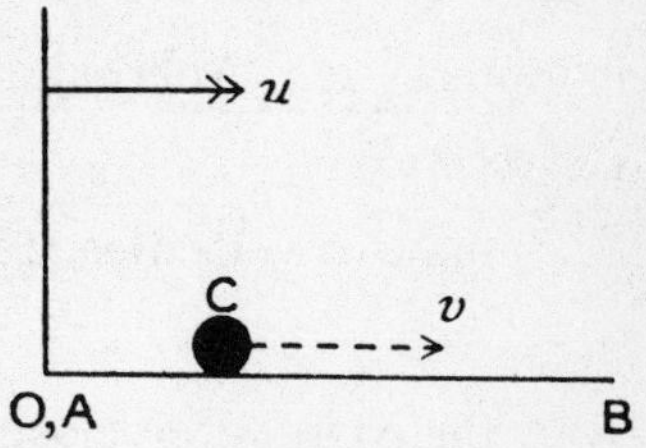

Suppose also that O says that the world of A, B is moving in the direction A→B at u luxes per second. What velocity does O assign to C?

O says that the journey to B occupies t seconds and is of length x luxes where (see p. 63)

$$x=\frac{x_1+ut_1}{\sqrt{1-u^2}} \text{ and } t=\frac{t_1+ux_1}{\sqrt{1-u^2}}.$$

99

∴ O says the velocity of C is $\frac{x}{t}$ luxes per second where

$$\frac{x}{t} = \frac{x_1 + ut_1}{t_1 + ux_1} = \frac{\frac{x_1}{t_1} + u}{1 + \frac{ux_1}{t_1}} = \frac{v+u}{1+uv}.$$

We may state this result as follows :

If a body C is moving at v luxes per second in the world of A along AB, and if the world of A is moving away from O in the direction A→B at u luxes per second, the velocity of C as measured by O is $\frac{u+v}{1+uv}$ luxes per second.

This result disagrees with the Newtonian method of composition of velocities. If a man is in a train travelling at 20 feet per second, and if he throws a bottle forward in the direction of motion of the train at 10 feet per second, we should expect a workman on the line to say that the bottle started moving at 20+10=30 feet per second. The formula just proved shows that it is not strictly accurate to combine the velocities by simple addition. But of course, for such small velocities as these, the correction is inappreciable. Approximately 1 foot per second $= \frac{1}{10^9}$ luxes per second

∴ the two velocities are $\frac{2}{10^8}$ and $\frac{1}{10^8}$ luxes per second

∴ the composite velocity is $\dfrac{\frac{2}{10^8} + \frac{1}{10^8}}{1 + \frac{2}{10^{16}}}$ luxes per second.

$$= \frac{\frac{3}{10^8}}{1 + \frac{2}{10^{16}}} \times 10^9 \text{ feet per second.}$$

$$= \frac{30}{1\cdot000,000,000,000,000,2} \text{ feet per second.}$$

which is indistinguishable from 30 feet per second.

But for particles moving at very high speeds, such as, for example, β particles emitted by radioactive substances, which can move with velocities as high as 0·99 luxes per second, the correction introduced by this formula is considerable.

It is interesting to take the extreme case where C is moving with the velocity of light, *i.e.* $v=1$.

The Newtonian law of composition would make O assess the velocity of C at $1+u$ luxes per second.   But the Relativity formula gives $\dfrac{1+u}{1+u}=1$ lux per second, so that O's measure is identical with A's measure.   This result is of course only a repetition of the statement which lies at the root of the whole theory—all observers alike who measure the velocity of light must obtain the same result.

Transverse Velocity.

Suppose, next, the body C starts from A at zero hour, and moves at a uniform rate at right angles to AB at w luxes per second.   What velocity does O assign to C ?

Suppose A says that C travels y_1 luxes in t_1 seconds.

$$\text{Then } w=\frac{y_1}{t_1}.$$

O says that C travels y luxes in t seconds, where

$$y=y_1 \text{ and } t=\frac{t_1+ux_1}{\sqrt{1-u^2}}.$$

But $x_1=0$, since A says that C moves at right angles to AB

$$\therefore t=\frac{t_1}{\sqrt{1-u^2}}$$

$$\therefore \frac{y}{t}=y_1\div\frac{t_1}{\sqrt{1-u^2}}=\sqrt{1-u^2}\times\frac{y_1}{t_1}=w\sqrt{1-u^2}$$

$\therefore$ O says that C moves with a velocity composed of $w\sqrt{1-u^2}$ luxes per second at right angles to AB, and u luxes per second along AB.

Lastly, suppose that A assigns to C a velocity of v luxes per second along AB, and w luxes per second at right angles to AB.   After t_1 seconds by A's clock, C has moved x_1 luxes in the direction AB and y_1 luxes in the direction perpendicular to AB, where $v = \dfrac{x_1}{t_1}$ and $w = \dfrac{y_1}{t_1}$.

O says that t seconds have elapsed, and that C has moved x luxes and y luxes in these two directions, where

$$x = \frac{x_1 + ut_1}{\sqrt{1 - u^2}}, \; y = y_1, \; t = \frac{t_1 + ux_1}{\sqrt{1 - u^2}}$$

$\therefore$ O says that C's velocity along AB is $\dfrac{x}{t}$ luxes per second, where as before

$$\frac{x}{t} = \frac{x_1 + ut_1}{t_1 + ux_1} = \frac{v + u}{1 + uv}$$

and that C's velocity perpendicular to AB is $\dfrac{y}{t}$ luxes per second, where

$$\frac{y}{t} = y_1 \div \frac{t_1 + ux_1}{\sqrt{1 - u^2}} = \sqrt{1 - u^2} \times \frac{y_1}{t_1 + ux_1}$$

$$= \sqrt{1 - u^2} \times \frac{\dfrac{y_1}{t_1}}{1 + \dfrac{ux_1}{t_1}} = \sqrt{1 - u^2} \times \frac{w}{1 + uv}$$

$\therefore$ C's velocity perpendicular to AB is

$$\frac{w\sqrt{1 - u^2}}{1 + uv} \text{ luxes per second.}$$

We see, therefore, that O's measure of C's transverse velocity depends on C's longitudinal velocity.

An interesting illustration of this law of composition of velocities is furnished by the motion of light through a moving medium.

Fresnel's Convection Coefficient.

The velocity of light depends on the medium through which it is propagated. In a vacuum it moves at 1 lux per second, and through air its velocity is nearly as great ; but for other media there may be considerable reductions. If the *refractive index* of a medium is μ, the velocity of light through this medium is $\frac{1}{\mu}$ luxes per second ; μ of course is always greater than 1, for water it is about 1·33.

Suppose a ray of light is transmitted through a stream of water, refractive index μ, which is itself travelling through a tube at u luxes per second in the direction of motion of the light-ray. With what velocity relative to the tube will the light-ray advance ?

If we regard the ether as stationary, we should expect the *motion* of the water to make no difference to the speed of advance of the light-ray. Its velocity in this case would be $\frac{1}{\mu}$ luxes per second.

If we regard the water as carrying the ether with it, the Newtonian law of composition of velocities would suggest that the rate of advance relative to the tube would be $\frac{1}{\mu}+u$ luxes per second.

Experiments by *Fizeau* in 1851 and by *Hoek* in 1868 showed that the actual rate of advance lay between these limits and amounted to $\frac{1}{\mu}+u\left(1-\frac{1}{\mu^2}\right)$ luxes per second. It was suggested by Fresnel that this was due to an ether-drag ; that, in other words, the ether was only partly carried along by the water-stream.

The Theory of Relativity supplies an alternative explanation. The light-ray is moving at $\frac{1}{\mu}$ luxes per second through the water, which is itself advancing at u luxes per second.

Therefore an outside observer, using the law of addition on p. 100, says that the velocity of the light-ray is

$$\frac{\frac{1}{\mu}+u}{1+\frac{u}{\mu}} \text{ luxes per second.}$$

Now $\dfrac{\frac{1}{\mu}+u}{1+\frac{u}{\mu}}=\dfrac{\left(\frac{1}{\mu}+u\right)\left(1-\frac{u}{\mu}\right)}{\left(1+\frac{u}{\mu}\right)\left(1-\frac{u}{\mu}\right)}=\dfrac{\frac{1}{\mu}+u-\frac{u}{\mu^2}-\frac{u^2}{\mu}}{1-\frac{u^2}{\mu^2}}.$

But u, the velocity of the stream of water in luxes per second, is very small. Consequently we shall obtain a good approximation if we neglect u^2.

In this case, the velocity becomes

$$\frac{1}{\mu}+u-\frac{u}{\mu^2}=\frac{1}{\mu}+u\left(1-\frac{1}{\mu^2}\right) \text{ luxes per second.}$$

This agrees with the expression required by experiment.

We therefore see that the experimental result is a close approximation to that deduced by using the Relativity formula. The expression $1-\dfrac{1}{\mu^2}$ is called Fresnel's Convection Coefficient. Details of Fizeau's and Hoek's experiments will be found in any standard text-book on *Light*.

Mass.

In the Newtonian System of Mechanics we assign to each body a number which measures a property of the body called its *mass*. The mass of a given body is regarded as a fixed thing, which is independent of its position or velocity, or indeed of any influence brought to bear on it so long as no part of the body disappears. *Newton* said that the mass of a body was the quantity of matter it contained : this phrase is not a definition, but it serves to suggest the nature of the concept which the word represents.

Newton's second law of motion states that the rate of change of "the quantity of motion" of a body is proportional to the impressed force, and this may be said to define either his conception of mass or his measure of force. From that law we see that if the "quantity of motion" of a body is defined by the product of its mass and its velocity, the increase in the quantity of motion per unit time is the measure of the force acting on the body. Instead of the phrase "quantity of motion," the term "momentum" is generally employed:

$$\text{momentum} = \text{mass} \times \text{velocity}.$$

This conception of momentum plays a very important part in Newtonian mechanics. If any number of bodies are in motion, and if there are no *external* forces acting upon the system, then the total momentum of the system remains constant. The bodies in the system may exert forces on each other, as, for example, by colliding; but such forces are not external and do not affect the sum-total of the momentum of the whole system. As the result of collisions, etc., there may be a transference of momentum from one member to another : the momentum which one body gives away is received by one or more other bodies of the system. But the quantity of motion or momentum of the system taken as a whole never varies unless some external force acts on the system and in this way contributes momentum to the system. Momentum is an asset for which an account can be kept. If a number of individuals each possess so much money and if this system of individuals neither receives money from outside nor pays away money to outsiders, but merely engages in internal financial transactions, the total capital of the system remains constant ; any individual member of the society can only increase his store of money at the expense of one or more other members. It may help the reader if we press this analogy still further.

We are comparing the total capital of a self-contained society and the number of members of that society with the total quantity of motion (or momentum) of a self-contained system of bodies and the number of bodies in the system. An observer who looks at the society may have a different standard of the value of money from that of its members. But his estimate of the total value of the capital of the society will remain the same, whatever interchanges of cash there are between the individual members. His total estimate may not agree with that made by another observer who has a different standard of values, but, whatever it is, it will remain the same as long as no new money is introduced into the system and no money is abstracted from the system. Again, the observer may see double : in that case he will, when counting the number of individuals in the society, obtain a different figure from that of an observer with normal vision. But as long as there are no births nor deaths, no emigrations or immigrations, his census figure will remain the same, however the members of the society behave. The observer is, in fact, applying a numerical measure to two properties of the society, namely, the capital the society possesses and the number of members of the society. Both of these things are part of the nature of the society, independent of any observer, although different observers may apply different systems of measurement. But under the conditions we have enumerated we may say that there is a Conservation of Capital and a Conservation of Membership of the Society.

So when dealing with any number of bodies, forming a self-contained system, and not subject to any external force, we shall say that there is a Conservation of Momentum and a Conservation of Mass. The estimate of each of these may vary from one observer to another, but whatever *internal* forces may be at work in the system causing redistribution of momentum or mass, we say that the estimates of the total momentum and the total mass made by any particular observer will remain constant.

Now let us suppose that the world of A, B contains two bodies of masses m_1, m_2, moving with velocities v_1, v_2 luxes per second in the direction A→B, and let us suppose that an observer O says that A's world is moving away from him in the direction A→B at u luxes per second.

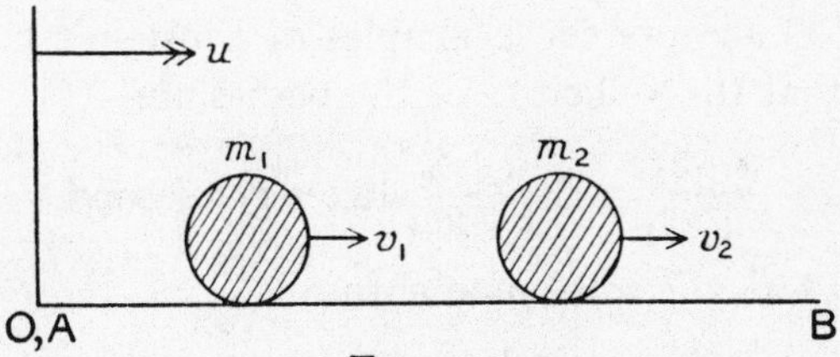

FIG. 31.

A says that the total mass of the system is

$$m_1 + m_2 = c, \text{ say,}$$

and the total momentum is $m_1 v_1 + m_2 v_2 = d$, say.

Now c and d are definite constants which will represent A's estimate of the total mass and total momentum of the system whatever happens to the bodies, given there are no external forces. The bodies may collide and so cause a transference of momentum ; the collision may break up one or both of the bodies into several pieces, etc. In spite of all this, taking the system as a whole, A will always obtain the same values for c and d : these values, therefore, correspond to some intrinsic property of the system.

Now if O accepted the principles of Newton's mechanics, he would agree with A that the total mass was always $m_1 + m_2 = c$, and he would say the total momentum was

$$m_1(u+v_1) + m_2(u+v_2)$$
$$= m_1 u + m_1 v_1 + m_2 u + m_2 v_2 = u(m_1+m_2) + m_1 v_1 + m_2 v_2$$
$$= uc + d.$$

O would therefore not agree with A's measure of the total momentum, but he would agree that the total momentum always remained the same whatever catastrophes occurred internally in the system. In other words, if a system is behaving so that one observer says that the total mass and the total momentum are each remaining constant, any other observer would agree with this statement, although he might disagree with the numerical values of the constants.

But if O accepts the principles of Einstein's mechanics, he says that the velocities of the bodies are

$$\frac{u+v_1}{1+uv_1} \text{ and } \frac{u+v_2}{1+uv_2} \text{ luxes per second,}$$

and therefore the total momentum is

$$\frac{m_1(u+v_1)}{1+uv_1} + \frac{m_2(u+v_2)}{1+uv_2}$$

which equals

$$u\left(\frac{m_1}{1+uv_1} + \frac{m_2}{1+uv_2}\right) + \left(\frac{m_1v_1}{1+uv_1} + \frac{m_2v_2}{1+uv_2}\right).$$

Now although, whatever catastrophes occur, the values of m_1+m_2 and $m_1v_1+m_2v_2$ remain unchanged, yet subject to these two conditions m_1, m_2, v_1, v_2 may vary in value in all sorts of ways. And we see that these two conditions are no longer sufficient to compel O's expression for the momentum to remain unchanged, for we cannot state it in terms of u, c, d only.

In other words, the fact that a system is behaving so that one observer says the total mass and the total momentum never alter is not sufficient to compel another observer to take the same view.

This means that we must surrender the principle of Conservation of Momentum as a property of a system, and make it depend on the standpoint of the observer. Such a sacrifice would rob mechanics of one of its most fundamental principles. Einstein makes this sacrifice unnecessary by introducing a new conception of Mass.

Einstein's Definition of Mass.

Instead of saying that the mass of a body is independent of its velocity, we shall say that if the mass of a body at rest in A's world is m, then if the body is moving at v luxes per second in A's world, its mass as measured by A is

$$\frac{m}{\sqrt{1-v^2}}.$$

It is interesting to note that, long before Einstein introduced this definition of mass, experimental work had suggested that the mass of bodies moving at very high velocities varied with the velocity. Sir J. J. Thomson's researches on the movements of electrons had shown that a high velocity caused an apparent increase of mass of amount $\frac{1}{2}mv^2$; and it can be shown (see Exercise VIII., No. 7) that if v is small $m+\frac{1}{2}mv^2$ is a close approximation to

$$\frac{m}{\sqrt{1-v^2}}.$$

Taking this definition of mass, it is now possible to prove that when one observer says that both the mass and the momentum of a system remain constant, all other observers will agree with him. Momentum is still defined as mass × velocity; therefore, if a body in A's world has a mass m when it is at rest, we see that when it is moving at v luxes per second in A's world, its mass is

$\dfrac{m}{\sqrt{1-v^2}}$ and its momentum is $\dfrac{mv}{\sqrt{1-v^2}}.$

Conservation of Mass and Momentum.

Using the same notation as on p. 107, A says that the total mass is

$$\frac{m_1}{\sqrt{1-v_1^2}} + \frac{m_2}{\sqrt{1-v_2^2}} = c, \text{ say };$$

and the total momentum is

$$\frac{m_1 v_1}{\sqrt{1-v_1^2}}+\frac{m_2 v_2}{\sqrt{1-v_2^2}}=d, \text{ say.}$$

Whatever (internal) vicissitudes the system undergoes, A will always compute the total mass as c and the total momentum as d.

Let us now examine O's calculations.

O says that the velocities of the bodies are

$$\frac{u+v_1}{1+uv_1}, \frac{u+v_2}{1+uv_2} \text{ luxes per second.}$$

The mass of the first body is therefore

$$\frac{m_1}{\sqrt{1-\left(\dfrac{u+v_1}{1+uv_1}\right)^2}}$$

Now $1-\left(\dfrac{u+v_1}{1+uv_1}\right)^2=\dfrac{(1+uv_1)^2-(u+v_1)^2}{(1+uv_1)^2}$

$$=\frac{1+2uv_1+u^2v_1^2-u^2-2uv_1-v_1^2}{(1+uv_1)^2}$$

$$=\frac{1-u^2-v_1^2+u^2v_1^2}{(1+uv_1)^2}=\frac{(1-u^2)(1-v_1^2)}{(1+uv_1)^2}.$$

$\therefore$ the mass of the first body is

$$m_1 \div \sqrt{\left\{\frac{(1-u^2)(1-v_1^2)}{(1+uv_1)^2}\right\}}=\frac{m_1(1+uv_1)}{\sqrt{1-u^2}\times\sqrt{1-v_1^2}}.$$

$\therefore$ the total mass

$$=\frac{m_1(1+uv_1)}{\sqrt{1-u^2}\times\sqrt{1-v_1^2}}+\frac{m_2(1+uv_2)}{\sqrt{1-u^2}\times\sqrt{1-v_2^2}}$$

$$=\frac{1}{\sqrt{1-u^2}}\left\{\frac{m_1+um_1v_1}{\sqrt{1-v_1^2}}+\frac{m_2+um_2v_2}{\sqrt{1-v_2^2}}\right\}$$

$$=\frac{1}{\sqrt{1-u^2}}\left\{\frac{m_1}{\sqrt{1-v_1^2}}+\frac{m_2}{\sqrt{1-v_2^2}}+u\left(\frac{m_1v_1}{\sqrt{1-v_1^2}}+\frac{m_2v_2}{\sqrt{1-v_2^2}}\right)\right\}$$

$$=\frac{1}{\sqrt{1-u^2}}\left\{c+ud\right\}.$$

∴ although O assigns a different value to the total mass from that assigned by A, as long as A finds that both the total mass and the total momentum remain constant, we see that O will also find that the total mass remains constant.

O also says that the momentum of the first body is

$$\frac{m_1}{\sqrt{1-\left(\frac{u+v_1}{1+uv_1}\right)^2}} \times \frac{u+v_1}{1+uv_1}.$$

Using the results just obtained, we see that this is equal to

$$\frac{m_1(1+uv_1)}{\sqrt{1-u^2}\times\sqrt{1-v_1{}^2}} \times \frac{u+v_1}{1+uv_1} \text{ or } \frac{m_1(u+v_1)}{\sqrt{1-u^2}\times\sqrt{1-v_1{}^2}}.$$

∴ the total momentum

$$=\frac{m_1(u+v_1)}{\sqrt{1-u^2}\times\sqrt{1-v_1{}^2}}+\frac{m_2(u+v_2)}{\sqrt{1-u^2}\times\sqrt{1-v_2{}^2}}$$

$$=\frac{1}{\sqrt{1-u^2}}\left\{u\left(\frac{m_1}{\sqrt{1-v_1{}^2}}+\frac{m_2}{\sqrt{1-v_2{}^2}}\right)+\left(\frac{m_1v_1}{\sqrt{1-v_1{}^2}}+\frac{m_2v_2}{\sqrt{1-v_2{}^2}}\right)\right\}$$

$$=\frac{1}{\sqrt{1-u^2}}\left\{uc+d\right\}.$$

∴ although O assigns a different value to the total momentum from that assigned by A, as long as A finds that both the total mass and total momentum remain constant, we see that O will also find the total momentum remains constant.

Hence, if we accept Einstein's definition of mass, we preserve both the Principle of the Conservation of Mass and the Principle of the Conservation of Momentum. Both mass and momentum are intrinsic properties of the system, existing independently of the observers, although different observers apply different standards of measurement to them.

The above discussion deals only with motion in the direction in which A's world is moving away from O. If a body at rest in A's world has a mass m, we say that its mass becomes $\frac{m}{\sqrt{1-v^2}}$ as computed by A when its velocity is v luxes per second in A's world, whatever the direction of motion of the body.   In order to establish the Conservation of Mass and Momentum in the general case, it is of course necessary to take account of the formula for the composition of transverse velocities ; the method is the same as before, but of course the actual algebra is modified.   We leave it as an exercise for the reader.

The term " proper mass " is applied to the mass-measure of a body at rest in the world in which its mass is computed. In the argument used above, m is the proper mass of the body in A's world.

When the body is at rest in A's world, O says that its mass is $\frac{m}{\sqrt{(1-u^2)}}$.   It has been pointed out on p. 109 that if u is small this is approximately equal to $m(1+\tfrac{1}{2}u^2)$ or $m+\tfrac{1}{2}mu^2$.

Readers acquainted with elementary mechanics will recognise that $\tfrac{1}{2}mu^2$ represents what is called the " kinetic energy " of the body—that is to say, the amount of work it is capable of doing by virtue of its motion.   The term " potential energy " is used for the work a body can do by virtue of its configuration—for example, a compressed spring is said to possess potential energy.   The mass of the body, which according to O is approximately $m+\tfrac{1}{2}mu^2$, is therefore equivalent to the sum of its proper mass and its kinetic energy.

The proper mass is therefore of the same nature as the kinetic energy, and we may think of this proper mass m as representing the potential energy of the body in the world in which it is at rest.

O's measure of the mass of the body is therefore the sum of its potential and kinetic energy ; and the fact that the

mass of a body increases with its velocity is equivalent to
the statement that an increase of (kinetic) energy shows
itself by an increase in apparent mass. This leads us to
identify mass with energy, and to treat the conservation of
mass as equivalent to the conservation of energy.

Momentum and Separation.

The comparative complication of the algebra we have
used to establish the conservation of mass and momentum
seems to make the simplicity of the result all the more
surprising. Was the new definition of mass a happy guess,
or was there some argument which indicated the form it
might be expected to take in order to assume an invariant
character when passing from one world to another?

If we replace velocity, which is displacement per unit
increase of time, by a displacement per unit increase
of separation, our new type of momentum for uniform
motion in A's world would be represented by $m \times \dfrac{x}{s}$
where $s^2 = t^2 - x^2$. We then have $\dfrac{s^2}{t^2} = 1 - \dfrac{x^2}{t^2} = 1 - v^2$

$$\therefore \frac{s}{t} = \sqrt{1 - v^2} \text{ or } \frac{t}{s} = \frac{1}{\sqrt{1 - v^2}}.$$

Hence $m \times \dfrac{x}{s} = m \times \dfrac{x}{t} \times \dfrac{t}{s}$

$$= m \times v \times \frac{1}{\sqrt{1 - v^2}} = \frac{mv}{\sqrt{1 - v^2}}$$

$$= \frac{m}{\sqrt{1 - v^2}} \times v.$$

If then m is the proper mass of a body in A's world, we
may say that the momentum of the body is

> *either* the proper mass × the displacement per unit
> increase of separation;
> *or* the modified mass × the displacement per unit
> increase of time.

In order to preserve the principle of Conservation of Momentum, we could therefore either modify our definition of Velocity or, as is done above, modify our definition of Mass.

The Principle of Restricted Relativity.

Throughout this book we have been continually examining various phenomena from the standpoints of different observers and attempting to co-ordinate the results recorded by these observers. If any law is enunciated which summarises physical processes, it is essential that its validity should be recognised by all observers alike. When such a law is expressed in mathematical form, it must retain that form when we pass from the axes of reference adopted by one observer to those adopted by another observer. In mathematical language, the form must be *invariant* for any necessary change of axes. We saw that the separation between two events was an invariant in this sense. Unless a law satisfies this condition, it cannot be true. This is Einstein's Principle of Relativity. Hitherto we have only considered worlds moving relatively to each other with *uniform* velocity ; and the existence of this limitation is indicated by referring to the subject as the *Restricted Theory of Relativity* ; its principles were enunciated by Einstein in 1905. The *General* Theory of Relativity takes into account the relations between worlds moving relatively to each other with variable velocity ; Einstein's investigation of this theory was not published till 1915, and owing to the War did not attract attention in England till 1917.

His Principle of Restricted Relativity may be stated as follows : Every law of Nature which holds good with respect to one co-ordinate system (say A's world) must also hold good for any other co-ordinate system (say O's world), provided that A's world and O's world are moving with uniform velocity relatively to one another.

This is equivalent to the statement that it is impossible to devise any experiment which will detect uniform motion through the ether. For, if a law was valid in one world only, it would indicate something unique in the nature of that world, and enable that world to be taken as a standard of reference. And equally if uniform motion through the ether could be detected, we should thereby possess a unique criterion for distinguishing one special world from all the others.

The purpose of the Theory of Relativity is to distinguish the subjective impressions of the observer and the relations which connect him with what he observes from the reality of the thing observed. The property of *separation* occupies a central position because it is a property of physical reality. The name " Relativity " is to some extent misleading, as it tends to imply that physical inquiry is of a relative nature. What Einstein has set himself to achieve is a formulation of physical principles which are independent of the observer. His work may, therefore, more justly be called a Theory of Physical Reality, or a Theory of Space-Time Events.

EXERCISE VIII

1. A body C is moving in the world of A along AB with a velocity $\frac{1}{2}$ lux per second ; O says that A's world is moving in the direction A→B at (i) $\frac{1}{2}$, (ii) $\frac{9}{10}$ lux per second. What is C's velocity according to O ?

2. Repeat No. 1, using the same data, except that C is moving in A's world in the direction B→A.

3. A body C is moving in the world of A at $\frac{1}{2}$ lux per second at right angles to AB ; O says that A's world is moving in the direction A→B at $\frac{3}{5}$ lux per second. What is C's velocity according to O ?

4. A body C at rest in A's world has a mass 2 as measured by A. If C now moves at $\frac{3}{5}$ lux per second along AB in A's

world, what is A's measure of its mass ?   If O says that
A's world is moving along AB at $\frac{1}{2}$ lux per second, what
is O's measure of its mass ?

5. If C is in motion with the data of No. 4, evaluate C's momentum as measured (i) by A, (ii) by O.

6. A body, whose proper mass is 5, is moving at 0·1 lux per
   second ; show that its apparent increase of mass is
   approximately equal to its kinetic energy (half mass ×
   velocity²).

7. Show that $(1 + \frac{1}{2}v^2)^2(1 - v^2) = 1 - \frac{3}{4}v^4 - \frac{1}{4}v^6$.   Hence if v^4 is
   small, show that $1 + \frac{1}{2}v^2$ is a close approximation to

$$\frac{1}{\sqrt{1 - v^2}}.$$

CHAPTER IX

GENERAL RELATIVITY

" I have made such wonderful discoveries that I am myself lost in astonishment : out of nothing I have created a new and another world."—JOHN BOLYAI ; a letter to his father on non-Euclidean Geometry, dated 3rd November 1823.

IN the restricted Theory of Relativity, we have considered only a special class of observers, namely, those who are moving relatively to the events observed with *uniform* velocity. In this theory we have seen that there is no justification for selecting any special observer as a Court of Appeal. It now becomes necessary to proceed to a more general inquiry. What differences arise if observers and events move relatively to each other with variable velocity ? Motion of this kind is of very common occurrence ; its investigation forms what is called the *general* Theory of Relativity.

Force and Acceleration.

If a stone is dropped from the top of a tower, it falls with a velocity which increases with the time. If we neglect air-resistance, the velocity increases at a constant rate : after 1 second its velocity is 32 feet per second, after 2 seconds its velocity is 64 feet per second, after 3 seconds its velocity is 96 feet per second, and so on. We say that the body is moving with *uniform acceleration,* and that its measure is 32 feet per second every second. The acceleration of a body is the *increase of its velocity per unit time.* If the velocity is diminishing, the acceleration is negative.

According to Newtonian mechanics, a body is accelerated (*i.e.* its velocity is changing in magnitude *or* direction *or* in both ways) *if and only if* a force is acting upon it ; and the magnitude of the force is represented by (i) the increase of momentum per unit time, or in other words (ii) mass ×increase of velocity per unit time, or in other words (iii) mass × acceleration.

If a body A pushes against a body B, it is easy to picture the nature of the force which A exerts on B. We can think of B as being struck by a very large number of molecules belonging to A, moving at very high speed and thereby transferring some of their own momentum to the molecules of B. Force exerted by what *appears* to be actual contact therefore seems an intelligible operation, and forces of this kind play a large part in ordinary life. The seat of the chair in which I am sitting is bombarding me with molecules, all giving me some of their momentum, and producing in me a consciousness of force which I call the pressure exerted by the chair. But this momentum I am receiving is spent as rapidly as it is given. What is the cause of the expenditure ? According to Newton, it is a force of attraction towards the centre of the Earth which the Earth exerts on me—the force of gravitation.

Clearly this is a force of an entirely different character ; it does not act by means of direct contact, but appears as an intangible influence radiating throughout space and diminishing inversely as the square of the distance from the source. Mention has already been made (see p. 6) of the difficulty, which familiarity has disguised, of accepting an hypothesis involving " Action at a Distance." But there is an even more remarkable property peculiar to gravitational forces.

Arrange an experiment so that two bodies are free to move under the gravitational attraction of the Earth, with no other forces influencing the motion. Newton took a closed cylinder in which he placed a feather and a guinea, and then exhausted the air from the cylinder. The two bodies were then allowed to fall simultaneously from the top of the cylinder. They fell side by side and struck the bottom at the same moment. Apart from the action of other forces, all bodies, however different in size, shape, or mass, fall with equal accelerations under the influence of gravity, provided they start from the same place. In other words, the acceleration of a body due to gravity depends solely on its position in space and is independent of size, shape, composition, and mass of the body. The acceleration is a function of position : near the Earth's surface we know by experiment that the acceleration is approximately 32 feet per second every second. Outside the Earth, the acceleration varies inversely as the square of the distance from the centre of the Earth. Taking the Earth's radius as 4000 miles, it follows that 8000 miles away from the Earth's centre the acceleration is $\frac{32}{2^2}=8$ feet per second every second, and at 12,000 miles from the Earth's centre it is $\frac{32}{3^2}=\frac{32}{9}=3\cdot6$ feet per second every second, and so on. If we limit our attention for the moment to bodies not more than a mile or two above the Earth's surface and within a mile or two of each other, we may regard the gravitational acceleration as practically uniform, and we shall say that the bodies are situated in a uniform field of force.

Fields of Force.

If an observer is watching a body in motion and notes that it is moving in a curve, he will say that there must be some force acting on it. This is required by Newton's Laws.

Suppose, however, some other onlooker, watching the

same series of events, says that the body is moving uniformly in a straight line and therefore is not subject to any force. Who is right ? Is it possible for two equally honest and competent observers to differ as to whether the path of the body is straight or curved ? Is it possible for the statements that (i) a force acts on the body, (ii) no force acts on the body, to be equally true ? Is it possible to say that one observer by virtue of his circumstances is better qualified than the other to judge what is happening ?

Suppose A lives in a large transparent airtight glass box, say the size of Olympia. A's home is taken to a place several thousand feet above the Earth's surface and allowed to fall. B stands on the ground and watches A's behaviour through a powerful telescope. For the sake of simplicity we shall suppose there is no air-resistance.

B's observations will be based on the fact that B regards himself as at rest on the Earth's surface and regards A as falling vertically with an acceleration of 32 feet per second every second. Everything in A's house is behaving in the same way—the pictures on the walls, the pipe in A's mouth, a tennis ball which A holds in one hand and a spring-balance which he holds in the other. When A throws the ball across the room, B says that the ball describes in space a curve called a parabola, the curve in which any projectile moves.

Now consider A's sensations. If A wishes to decorate a wall of his room with a picture, he holds it up against the wall and leaves it there ; there is no need to suspend it from a hook ; when he takes his hand away, the picture remains where he has put it. B, of course, says that the wall and the picture both fall at the same rate. A takes his pipe out of his mouth and drops it, but the pipe remains stationary. B says that both the pipe and A fall side by side. When A throws the ball across the room, he judges that it moves in a straight line until it collides with some object in the room, although B says its path is curved. A attaches a table to the spring-balance and notes that its weight is zero; he then stands on the platform of a weighing-machine and observes that his own weight is zero. All these experiments convince A that he is at rest in a space free of gravitational attraction, while B is equally convinced that A is falling in a uniform field of force. Previous discussions in this book make it easy to reconcile the discrepancy between the opinions of A and B. Whereas B chooses axes of reference attached to the Earth, A takes axes of reference attached to the glass box. These two systems are moving relatively to each other with uniform acceleration; and the consequence of this is that a path A calls straight, B says is curved, and a region which A declares is free of force, B says is a uniform field of force. The relation is reciprocal: A says that the Earth and B are falling towards him with a uniform acceleration. If B rolls a ball across a level table, A says that the ball actually describes a parabola in space, and so on.

The Principle of Equivalence.

Our natural inclination is to associate ourselves with B's view rather than A's, but this is a parochial attitude, and is due to the fact that we are accustomed to live under the same conditions as B does. If, however, we were a race of falling aviators we should sympathise with A rather than B. The Theory of Relativity forbids us to prefer any one observer to any other; there is to be no favouritism or prejudice: any law of Nature must be equally acceptable to all observers, and must therefore take an invariant form which survives transformation from one world to another. Gravitational force is an illusion. This does not, of course, mean that if you throw yourself off the top of a tower, trouble will not ensue. But Einstein denies that the event consisting in your subsequent collision with the ground is caused by the Earth exerting an attractive force on you. We shall soon be in a position to give Einstein's explanation of the course of events.

So far we have only considered the effect of gravitation over a small region throughout which the Newtonian theory regards it as setting up a uniform field of force. We have seen that in this case the effects can all be removed by a change of axes. The existence of a uniform field of force as affirmed by B is denied by A, who chooses axes moving with uniform acceleration relative to B's axes. Another observer with a different system of axes would affirm the existence of a different field of force. Consequently we may say that these fields of force are imputed by the observer to the Universe owing to his own local circumstances. A suitable change of axes will neutralise any uniform field of force. It therefore follows that a *uniform* field of force is artificial, an unconscious invention of the observer, rather than a property of the thing observed.

A has by his choice of axes neutralised in his own neighbourhood what B calls a gravitational field, but in so doing he has made B appear to be falling toward him with an acceleration 32 feet per second every second, and if he can see through the Earth and observe another aviator C crashing there, he will impute to C an acceleration of 64 feet per second every second. A therefore says that B is in a field of force and C in another field of double the intensity : similarly with other falling aviators elsewhere, A will impute to each a field of force of different intensity and direction. Consequently, although A's choice of axes removes the effect of gravitation in his own neighbourhood, it makes matters worse elsewhere, by creating fields of force of all sorts of various magnitudes and directions. However, that does not perhaps matter to A. The conclusion of these remarks forms Einstein's Principle of Equivalence :

If attention is confined to a small region of space, a gravitational field at rest is equivalent to a frame of reference moving with uniform acceleration in a field free of gravitation ; and it is impossible to devise any experiment which will distinguish between the two.

We therefore see that although the presence of matter is responsible for creating a gravitational field, yet any observer, just like the inhabitant of the glass box, can so choose his axes that *in his immediate neighbourhood* all gravitational effects are neutralised, and consequently, within this small region, although not beyond it, the principles of the theory of *restricted* Relativity apply. This conclusion is of the utmost importance, because it enables us to use within these limits results established for space-time uninfluenced by matter.

Space-Time Distortion.

Let us now consider the world-line of a body moving through a space-time domain, in which matter is present, and let us suppose that an observer is moving with, in fact travelling on, the body. At each point in space-time, the observer by his choice of axes can and does neutralise the gravitational field in his immediate neighbourhood. He can use his own clock to measure the separation of two events in his career if these events are very close together ; the separation will be simply the proper time as recorded by his clock. By a process of summation he will then find the total measure of the separation between any two events in his career, measured along his world-line. If the body is moving freely, the observer moving with it says that the world-line is straight, and consequently that the path in space-time is such that the separation between two events is a maximum. If then the measure of the separation is the same for all observers, the path must be such that every other observer will find that the separation measured along it is a maximum. But other observers will not say that the world-line is straight; from their points of view the principles of the *restricted* theory do not apply. The fact that the geodesic, *i.e.* the route for maximum separation, is a straight line depends on the restricted theory where space-time is uniform. This is no longer true.

The other observers say that the presence of matter has distorted space-time in its neighbourhood, and as a result of this the geodesic is a curve. According to Newton, the Earth describes an ellipse round the Sun owing to an attractive force which the Sun exerts on the Earth. But according to Einstein the presence of the Sun causes irregularities in the space-time in its neighbourhood, and the Earth simply picks its way through this tangled domain following a path (can we call it a spiral ellipse in space-time?) so devised that when we allow for the crumpling up of space-time the separation measured along it between any two given events is a maximum. In other words, the Earth's orbit is curved not because the Sun exerts any force on it, but because in the distorted space-time domain round the Sun the geodesic is not straight but curved : it is easier to move through the obstacles by following a curved route, just as in passing through a wood in which the trees are denser in some parts than others it is often easier to follow a curved route than to try to go straight ahead all the time.

This conception of distorted space may be easier to appreciate by considering another illustration of a field of force.

Life on a Rotating Disc.

Imagine a large plane disc, centre C, which an outside observer O says is rotating about an axis through C perpendicular to its plane. Another observer A lives on the disc and draws through C axes of reference on the disc along and perpendicular to CA.

A regards the disc as at rest, and thinks that O is moving in a circle in the reverse direction. But A realises that he has to attach himself to the disc in order to keep his footing. A believes that there is a gravitational field of force acting outwards from C and proportional to the distance from C. But O says that A is travelling round C in a circle with uniform speed ; and therefore

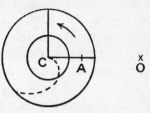

FIG. 32.

has an acceleration towards C which is produced by A holding on to the disc, just as a stone attached to the end of a string and whirled round in a circle is held to its circular path by the pull of the string. Suppose now a body starts from C and moves with uniform velocity along CO towards O. Then of course O says that it is travelling in a straight line in a field devoid of force. How will A view the progress of the body ? A thinks that the disc is at rest and that it is O who is revolving. Consequently A will say that the body travels outwards from C along the line CO, which is itself rotating. A therefore, tracing the position of the body relative to his axes on the disc, says that the body describes a sort of spiral curve ; and naturally he attributes the curved orbit to the gravitational field which he believes is existing. What therefore O regards as a straight path in a field of no force, A regards as a curved path in a gravitational field.

Suppose now a circle is drawn on the disc with C as centre, and that A uses his rule to measure (i) its diameter, (ii) its circumference. Suppose that A finds the diameter is equal to 1,000,000 lengths of his rule, O will agree with this measurement, because in any radial position the rule has no velocity in the direction of its length, relative to O. But when A places the rule tangentially to the circle and proceeds to measure the circumference by stepping it off in small bits, the rule has a velocity in the direction of its length relative to O, and therefore O says that the rule contracts. O knows that the circumference of the circle is equal to $\pi \times$ diameter, where $\pi = 3 \cdot 14159265 \ldots$, and therefore 3,141,592 steps would be required to traverse the circumference if the rule did not contract, but owing to the contraction more steps will be necessary ; the number of course depends on the contraction ratio. O watches A perform the process, and notes that it takes (say) 3,300,000 steps, using the contracted rule. O and A must of course agree in any counting process. A is surprised by this result, because he is unconscious of any contraction of the rule, and is forced to believe that the ratio of the circumference to the diameter is no longer $3 \cdot 14159 \ldots$, but is in this case $3 \cdot 3$.

A now repeats the process with a larger concentric circle ; suppose its diameter is double that of the first circle. O and A then agree that the diameter is 2,000,000 steps of the rule. O says that the speed of A is now twice what it was before, and therefore the contraction-ratio is greater than before, and so it now takes 8,000,000 steps of the rule to measure round the circumference (see Exercise IX., No. 7). A is therefore compelled to say that the ratio of the circumference to the diameter is $\dfrac{8,000,000}{2,000,000} = 4$.

We see, then, that in A's world the circumference of a circle is not proportional to the diameter ; in other words, two circles of different size are *not* similar (*i.e.* are not the same shape). A's geometry does not therefore agree with the geometry of Euclid, and we say that A's space is non-Euclidean.

But there is also another curious feature of A's world. Since the velocity of A relative to O increases proportionally to the distance of A from the centre C, O says that the clocks in A's world do not run at the same rate ; the farther a clock is from C, the slower it runs according to O. Time-measure, as judged by O, is therefore not uniform in A's world. In the restricted theory we saw that O said A failed to synchronise his clocks and that all the clocks ran slow, but O admitted that they all ran at the same rate : time was uniform all over A's world, although its measure was different from that used by O. Here, however, there is a new element of irregularity, for A's clocks run at a rate which depends on their distance from C.

The irregularity of space-measurement is also accompanied by an irregularity of time-measurement. The space-time world of A is distorted, both in respect of time and in respect of space.

O, of course, considers that both space and time are uniform : the non-Euclidean character of A's space and the irregularity of time are due to A's creation of a gravitational field, arising from his choice of axes. O's choice of axes has made the space-time domain uniform; A's choice of axes is equivalent to setting up a gravitational field which shows itself in the distortion of space and time.

Gravitational Fields.

The existence of matter gives rise to a gravitational field in its neighbourhood ; but instead of saying that this is a field of force, we now say that it is a distortion of space-time. The invariant expression for the separation between two events, $s^2 = t^2 - x^2 - y^2 - z^2$, was established by assuming that space-time is uniform : since in the neighbourhood of matter this is no longer the case, this expression will require modification in a gravitational field, if it is to survive transformation from one world to another. A new geometry is automatically imposed upon us, with a different set of mensuration formulæ. Various systems of geometry have been investigated during the last hundred years.

Up till that time it had been assumed that the geometry of Euclid was the only possible logical system. The characteristic property of Euclid's geometry is that the sum of the angles of a triangle is two right angles. It is now universally accepted that equally consistent Geometries exist which conflict with Euclid. In what is called *Hyperbolic Geometry* the angle sum of every triangle is less than two right angles, and in *Elliptic Geometry* the angle sum is always greater than two right angles. If we ask which of these is really true, the question can only mean, which of these applies to the world in which we live. *Gauss* attempted to answer the question by taking a large triangle whose corners were the summits of three mountains and measuring the angles. But the difference of their sum from two right angles was less than probable experimental errors. There is no doubt that only a triangle whose sides involve lengths of astronomical magnitude can give a decisive answer to an inquiry conducted in this way. Gauss's experiment could not possibly lead to a decision. Such evidence as exists at the present time points to the theory that the geometry of our Universe is Elliptic, and this involves the supposition that it is finite in extent, finite but unbounded, just as the surface of a sphere is finite but without a boundary.

The educated man of to-day understands the general characteristics of the Newtonian theory, but only the specialist can read and understand the *Principia* in which the formal investigation is made. In the same way the mathematical process used by Einstein to deduce the laws of the space-time geometry of our Universe and the formulation of those laws in all their generality can only be appreciated and apprehended by the mathematical specialist. But the nature of the ideas which distinguish Einstein's theory from Newton's can be illustrated without any advanced mathematical reasoning, and it is possible to state in a simple form Einstein's law of gravitation for the special case which affects us most, namely, for the portion of space-time round about the Sun.

Suppose that S is the centre of a massive body such as the Sun, and suppose that P and Q are two events near together in space and time. From Q draw the perpendicular QN to SP, produced if necessary. Since Q is near P, we regard QN and PN as small compared with SP, and the length of each is to be measured in luxes. Suppose also that the time-interval from P to Q is t seconds where t is also small. Then

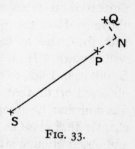

FIG. 33.

if m is the gravitational mass of the massive body at S, also measured in luxes, the separation of Q from P is given by

$$s^2 = \left(1 - \frac{2m}{SP}\right)t^2 - QN^2 - \left(1 + \frac{2m}{SP}\right) . PN^2.$$

The method for calculating m is shown in Exercise IX., Nos. 5, 6. For the Sun, $m = 0\cdot000,004,9$, and for the Earth $m = 0\cdot000,000,000,02$. It should be noted that if $m = 0$, this expression becomes $s^2 = t^2 - QN^2 - PN^2 = t^2 - PQ^2$, which is the ordinary form for the separation in the restricted theory : putting m equal to zero is of course equivalent to saying that no matter is present to influence the nature of the space-time in which the events occur. The introduction of the additional terms involving m therefore represent the changes in the mensuration formulæ caused by the distortion of the space-time domain surrounding a single massive body.

If a body is moving freely in the neighbourhood of a massive body, it follows a path so chosen that the separation, as determined by the formula given above and measured along this path, is a maximum. Newton's Law of Gravitation is replaced by Einstein's geometrical mensuration formula for a space-time domain, a geometrical space-time Law. Einstein's Law may be tested by examining the paths in which the planets move round the Sun. Are these paths geodesics in space-time, when the separation is calculated according to the formula given above ? That the paths of the planets fit very closely with the paths as calculated in the Newtonian theory is well known. It is simply because Newton's Law of Gravitation leads to orbits which agree so closely with the observed orbits that up till the time of Einstein this law was universally accepted. But we shall see in the next chapter that close as is the agreement between calculation and observation, a still higher degree of accuracy is secured by the substitution of Einstein's Geometrical Law for Newton's Mechanical Law : the latter may indeed be regarded as a first approximation towards the former.

EXERCISE IX

1. A toy pistol is pointed straight at the bull's-eye of a target. At the moment the pellet leaves the pistol, the target is allowed to fall vertically. Will the pellet strike the bull's-eye, if air resistance is ignored ? Compare the views of the path traced out by the pellet formed by (i) the boy who holds the pistol, (ii) a microbe on the bull's-eye.

2. Suppose that A, whose weight is 10 stone when on the ground, is standing on a weighing-machine in his glass box (p. 120), and notices that his weight has changed from zero (i) to 10 stone, (ii) to 20 stone, (iii) to 100 stone, what will he say about gravitation ? How will B, who is standing on the ground, account for it ?

3. Three people are watching a body. One says it is at rest, the second says it is moving in a straight line, and the third says it is moving in a curve. Is it possible that all three observers are equally efficient ?

4. Suppose that the disc on p. 125 is rotating at the rate of

5 revolutions per minute, and that a body is moving at a uniform rate of 5 feet per minute just above the disc along the straight line CO. Plot its positions at intervals of 1 second for 12 seconds, *as recorded by A*, who uses lines marked on the disc as axes of reference.

5. If the gravitational mass of the Sun is m, the acceleration towards the Sun of a planet at a distance of r luxes from the centre of the Sun is approximately $\frac{m}{r^2}$. If the planet is moving in its orbit at v luxes per second, it is known that the acceleration radially inwards is $\frac{v^2}{r}$. Hence $\frac{m}{r^2} = \frac{v^2}{r}$ or $m = v^2 r$. Taking the distance of the Earth from the Sun as 500 luxes, use this formula to show that the gravitational mass of the Sun is about 1·5 km., and express the result in luxes.

6. Taking the distance of the Moon from the Earth as 240,000 miles and the period of a revolution as $27\frac{1}{3}$ days, use the formula in No. 5 to show that the gravitational mass of the Earth is about 5 millimetres, and express the result also in luxes. [1 lux = 186,000 miles.]

7. In the measurement of the circumferences of the two circles on the rotating disc on p. 126, show according to O that (i) the first speed of A is given by $1 - u^2 = \left(\frac{314}{330}\right)^2$, (ii) the contraction-ratio along the larger circle is about 0·79, (iii) the number of steps of the rule round the larger circle is about 7,970,000.

CHAPTER X

THE EINSTEIN TESTS

" In one sense deductive theory is the enemy of experimental physics. The latter is always striving to settle by crucial tests the nature of the fundamental things : the former strives to minimise the successes obtained by showing how wide a nature of things is compatible with all experimental results.—A. S. EDDINGTON, *Mathematical Theory of Relativity*.

A SCIENTIFIC theory maintains its position only so long as it harmonises observed facts. If discrepancies between theory and observation remain, after full allowance has been made for possible observational errors, then modifications must be made in the theory.

The Perihelion of Mercury.

For a long time it had been realised that there was a serious difference between the observed orbit of Mercury and the path obtained by calculations based on Newton's Law of Gravitation. If Mercury were the only planet in the solar system, its path would be an oval curve called an ellipse having the Sun at a point inside it known as the focus S ; the centre C of the curve is a different point ; if CS cuts the orbit at A, A' as shown, then the planet is nearest the Sun when at A and is farthest from the Sun when at A'. The point A is called the

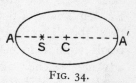

FIG. 34.

perihelion of the orbit. Owing to the attraction exerted by the other planets, using Newtonian language, the regularity of motion is upset, and instead of moving in exactly the same elliptic orbit, year after year, the path is represented by an ellipse in which the perihelion is steadily advancing, *i.e.* SA is steadily rotating relatively to the fixed stars. Calculations reposing on Newton's Law of Gravitation show that the combined influence of all the known planets would cause a rotation of 532 seconds of angle per century. Observation, however, shows that it is actually rotating at the rate of 574 seconds per century. There is consequently a discrepancy of 42 seconds per century to be accounted for. This may sound a very small error—it is less than the angle which a halfpenny subtends at the eye from a distance of 135 yards—but actually it is far greater than any possible observational error.

The irregularities in the motion of Uranus were responsible for the dramatic discovery of Neptune. In 1846, Adams and Le Verrier, working independently, calculated the path of a planet which would produce the observed perturbations in the orbit of Uranus. The calculated position in the sky of this hypothetical planet was sent by Le Verrier to Dr. Galle of Berlin, who at once turned his telescope to the place indicated in the sky and discovered the new planet Neptune very close to the position predicted for it. An attempt was made to account for the irregularity in Mercury's motion in a similar fashion : and a planet to which the name *Vulcan* was given was invented for the purpose. But Vulcan has never been found, and its existence is now discredited. If, however, we substitute Einstein's Law of Space-time for Newton's Law of Gravitation, the discrepancy disappears. The deduction of this result from Einstein's Law requires mathematics of too advanced a character for these pages, but the additional correction which Einstein's Law supplies can be stated in simple language : if a planet describes its orbit with a speed of v luxes per second, the line joining the Sun to the perihelion rotates through an additional angle of amount $12v^2$ right angles per revolution. The reader can easily verify (see Exercise X., No. 3) that in the case of Mercury this correction amounts to within a second of the needed 42 seconds per century.

It is very unfortunate that it is impossible to check this correction by reference to any of the other planets. For in the case of every other planet either the speed is too small or else the orbit is so nearly circular that accurate observation of the position of the perihelion is impossible. But the fact that it gives so accurately the necessary correction for Mercury's motion is a powerful and striking argument in favour of the Relativity theory.

In addition to showing how his theory removed an anomaly of which no satisfactory explanation had previously been given, Einstein made two predictions which, if capable of being submitted to an experimental test, would serve to distinguish between the old theory and the new.

Shift of Spectral Lines.

The vibration of an atom may be regarded as supplying us with an ideal natural clock. If two atoms are identical, and if we measure the separation between the beginning and end of a vibration, the result should be the same wherever the atoms are situated. Now suppose one of the atoms is close to the surface of the Sun and that the other is in a laboratory on the Earth. We may regard the events for each atom as happening at the same places.

Suppose that the period of vibration of the solar atom is t_1 seconds, and for the terrestrial atom is t_2 seconds, then, for the solar atom, $s^2 = \left(1 - \frac{2m}{\mathrm{SP}}\right)t_1^2$

where SP$=430,000$ miles$=2\cdot3$ luxes, $m=0\cdot000,004,9$ luxes.

And for the terrestrial atom, $s^2=\left(1-\dfrac{2m}{SQ}\right)t_2{}^2$

where SQ$=93,000,000$ miles$=500$ luxes,
$m=0\cdot000,004,9$ luxes.

The value of s is the same in each case

$$\therefore \left(1-\frac{2m}{2\cdot3}\right)t_1{}^2=\left(1-\frac{2m}{500}\right)t_2{}^2, \text{ where } m=0\cdot000,004,9.$$

It is, therefore, clear that t_1 is a little greater than t_2. The reader may see for himself that $\dfrac{t_1}{t_2}$ is approximately $1\cdot000,002$. Consequently the solar atom vibrates just a little more slowly than the atom on the Earth. Now the time of vibration affects the colour, and therefore in the solar spectrum there should be a very small shift towards the red end of the spectrum as compared with the spectrum of the same atom on the Earth.

The shift is, however, in general so minute as to defy measurement. But Professor Eddington pointed out some time ago a case where a larger shift might be expected. There is a companion star of Sirius, known as a " white dwarf," *i.e.* an early type of star of very low intrinsic brightness. It is believed that the density of this star (the statement sounds incredible !) is more than 30,000 times the density of water—that is to say, its mass is more than half a ton per cubic inch ; its radius is about 12,000 miles. Consequently it sets up a gravitational field of so great an intensity in its neighbourhood that a measurable shift is likely to occur. Mr. Adams of Mount Wilson Observatory has recently obtained results for the displacement of some of the hydrogen lines of the spectrum of this star, which appear to confirm the Einstein prediction, although the method involved considerable difficulties both of observation and measurement.

Curvature of Light-Rays.

Newton envisaged the possibility that light has weight. It is now an accepted fact that a ray of light does exert radiation pressure on any object on which it impinges : this is equivalent to saying that light possesses mass. Naturally the quantities involved are small : Professor Eddington, in his volume *Space, Time, and Gravitation*, states that the mass of the total amount of sunlight impinging on the Earth every twenty-four hours is about 160 tons. But if light has mass, whether we follow Newton's or Einstein's Law, a ray of light passing near the Sun should move in a curve in just the same way as do the planets or comets. The fact that light moves so much faster than any planet or comet will naturally mean that the amount of the deflection when passing near the Sun is very much less.

If, then, a ray of light travelling from a star P towards the Earth E passes near the Sun S and is slightly deflected so that ES is not in the same straight line with SP, then the star, as seen from the Earth, will appear to be in the direction

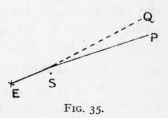

FIG. 35.

ESQ, whereas its true direction is the line EP. The angular displacement between the true position and the apparent position of the star in the sky is represented by the angle PEQ. This angular displacement can be calculated, but different results are obtained according as we adopt Newton's or Einstein's Law. It has already been pointed out that Newton's Law may be regarded as a first approximation to Einstein's Law. The latter, so to speak, adds on to Newton's Law a correction arising from the distortion of space in the neighbourhood of matter.

If we were to replace the formula on p. 129 by the relation $s^2 = \left(1 - \dfrac{2m}{\text{SP}}\right)t^2 - \text{QN}^2 - \text{PN}^2$, we should obtain orbits which agree closely with those deduced from Newtonian principles. The addition of the term $-\dfrac{2m}{\text{SP}} \cdot \text{PN}^2$ corresponds to a substitution of non-Euclidean for Euclidean space (not space-time), and it is the presence of this term which makes a decisive difference between the calculated value of the apparent displacement of a star in the two theories. It is impossible to reproduce the necessary calculations in these pages, but the result can be stated in a simple form. If a ray of light from a star passes the Sun at a distance r luxes from the centre of the Sun, then, as viewed from the Earth, the angular displacement according to the Einstein theory is $\dfrac{8m}{\pi r}$ right angles, where as before $m = 0.000,004,9$ and $\pi = 3.14$. If the ray passes close to the Sun's surface we may take $r = 700,000$ km. $= 2.3$ luxes. We leave it to the reader (Exercise X., No. 4) to show that this is equivalent to an angle of about 1.75 seconds. The Newtonian theory, on the other hand, leads to a displacement of $\dfrac{4m}{\pi r}$ right angles, just half the amount required by Einstein. It lies with the astronomer by actual observation to judge which is correct.

Sir Oliver Lodge, in the course of an article in the *Nineteenth Century*, gave a vivid illustration of the task this test imposes on the practical astronomer ; part of it we venture to quote :

" Take a fine silk thread of indefinite length and stretch it straight over the surface of a smooth table. Imagine a star at one end of the thread and an eye at the other end, and let the thread typify one of the rays of light emitted from the star. Now take a halfpenny and place it on the table close to the thread so that the eye end of the thread is 10 feet away ; and then push the halfpenny gently forward till it has displaced the thread the barely perceptible amount of $\frac{1}{1000}$ inch. The eye, looking along the thread, will now see that the ray is no longer absolutely straight ; in other words, the star whose apparent position is determined by that ray will appear slightly shifted. The scale is fixed by the size of the halfpenny, whose diameter, 1 inch, is used to represent the Sun's diameter of 800,000 miles. The 10-foot distance between eye and Sun practically supposes the eye is on the Earth, which would be a spot about the size of this full stop. As for the distance of the star at the far end of the thread, that does not matter in the least ; but on the same scale for one of the nearest stars the thread would have to be about a thousand miles long. The shift of $\frac{1}{1000}$ inch at a distance of 10 feet corresponds to an angle of $1\frac{3}{4}$ seconds, which is just the optical shift that ought to occur, according to Einstein, when a ray from the star nearly grazes the Sun's limb on its way to a telescope."

Modern apparatus and methods have now attained such a high degree of refinement that the measurement of even so small an angular displacement as is indicated by this illustration, or rather the discrimination between two small angular displacements of this order of magnitude, is well within the powers of the present-day astronomer. Unfortunately the only time when a star nearly in line with the Sun is visible is during a total solar eclipse, and, in addition to this, clear observations are difficult to obtain unless there happen to be at the time of the eclipse several bright stars in the direction under survey. By good fortune, a total solar eclipse occurred on May 29, 1919, when these conditions were satisfied. Two expeditions were organised, one being sent to *Sobral*, in North Brazil, and the other to *Principe*, in the Gulf of Guinea, to take the necessary photographs. The story of these expeditions has been told in detail by Professor Eddington (see *Space, Time, and Gravitation*, ch. vii.) ; the expedition to Principe fared badly, because clouds interfered seriously with the operations, but at Sobral the atmospheric conditions were excellent. Here, however, there were other complications which diminished the value of many of the photographs. Allowing for probable experimental errors, the Principe observations gave an apparent displacement of between 1·91 and 1·31 seconds, while the Sobral observations gave a displacement between 2·10 and 1·86 seconds. Another total eclipse occurred in 1922, and a successful expedition was organised by the Lick Observatory. The published results of one set of photographs (*Lick Observatory Bulletin*, No. 346) give the mean value as 1·72 seconds (or if a certain correction is applied as 2·05 seconds) with a possible error in defect or excess of about 0·12 seconds. It is believed that the records of another set of photographs, not yet published, are even more favourable to the Einstein deflection. There will be another very favourable solar eclipse in 1938.

Many readers may feel disappointed that there should appear to be so wide a margin in the recorded results. It is necessary to engage in practical work to appreciate that sources of experimental error are inevitable : all that can be done is to indicate the probable margin of error. It is also necessary to remember that the conditions under which an expedition has to work are far less favourable than those of a permanent observatory, just as a field telephone company on active service is far less favourably placed than a London Telephone Exchange. But the records undoubtedly support Einstein as opposed to Newton. If it is necessary to choose between the two, there can be no doubt that the Einstein calculations are in closer agreement with eclipse observations than those based on the Newtonian theory. But apart from the concrete evidence furnished by observation, it is important to remember that the deflection had not been suspected until Einstein predicted it as a consequence of Relativity. A theory which predicts a hitherto unknown phenomenon afterwards verified by observation stands on firmer ground than a theory invented to account for some known observational effect, mainly because there is usually a variety of different hypotheses which can be suggested to fit a given frame of facts. And whatever modifications future research may require, nothing can obscure the dramatic character of the success which has attended this prediction, made by Einstein in 1915, and tested by astronomers at the eclipses of 1919 and 1922, and now generally accepted as fulfilled.

General Conclusions.

The Restricted Theory of Relativity may be regarded as complete : future investigations will add nothing to it. If we accept the two fundamental axioms on which it is based, the conclusions follow as a matter of formal logic. In process of time the characteristic ideas of the theory will become familiar to the man in the street, their acceptance will then become a matter of course, and their revolutionary nature will be forgotten. If intercourse should ever become practicable between beings in worlds separating with velocities comparable with that of light, the theory would seriously affect conduct, but this contingency seems so remote and improbable that it may safely be discounted.

The General Theory of Relativity may in a sense be said to be still in the making. Certainly its implications are far more controversial. To say that Einstein's Law of Space-time has superseded Newton's Law of Gravitation is not the same as affirming that Einstein's theory fits in with all the phenomena of modern physics. No link has, for example, yet been forged between the theory of Relativity and the Quantum theory. But if we accept the principles of Restricted Relativity, Newton's Law of Gravitation cannot stand in its existing form for the simple reason that it is ambiguous. Apart from the doubt in the Newtonian expression $\frac{mm'}{r^2}$ as to the meaning of *mass*, which arises because the mass changes with the velocity, we have seen that the value of r also depends on the circumstances of the observer.

The universality of character which was the most striking feature of the law has therefore disappeared. No doubt the statement by which the law is expressed could be modified so as to remove these difficulties of interpretation. It is not, however, worth while attempting to do so, because it cannot in any case be expressed in a form which will be true for all observers. It is not therefore the kind of law which our previous discussions have shown a law of Nature should be ; at the same time calculations based on it give results which agree closely with those deduced from Einstein's general theory. Formally the two theories have nothing in common ; they are built upon contrary hypotheses. Newton assumes an absolute space and an absolute time, and his laws of motion are bound up with these hypotheses. Einstein treats these suppositions as untrue, and creates a space-time (*not* a space and time) domain. The great achievement in his theory is the fact that he is able independently of axes of reference to identify a unique track in space-time uniting two events, the generalisation of a straight line in Euclid, and to specify this path both in a field devoid of matter and in a field influenced by matter. The theory of Relativity, whether restricted or general, is a theory of geodesics. The treatment in this book is confined to those aspects of the subject which may reasonably be regarded as established or at least supported by strong evidence, although further investigations may introduce minor modifications. But the theory has led physicists to formulate further hypotheses which at present must be considered mainly speculative. What is the nature of the structure of the Universe ; is it finite or infinite, is it continuous or discrete, is its substance matter or events ? Some, perhaps all, of these questions may never receive a final and complete answer. In regard to the first of these inquiries there is, however, a slight balance of evidence in favour of supposing that the Universe is finite, but of course unbounded, and an estimate of its size is expressed by the statement that a ray of light emitted from a source would, if unimpeded, travel round the Universe and return to its point of departure after a thousand million years. It is not inconceivable that science may at some future time be able to devise and execute a practical test which will decide the question. But this is a superficial type of knowledge. The theory of Relativity may describe the laws which reality obeys, and trace its structure : this indeed is all it sets out to do. Of the inner nature of things, it says nothing : this is left to the philosopher, who says a great deal, but in the end we never appear to be much, if any, the better for it.

EXERCISE X

1. At what distance would a halfpenny (diameter 1 inch) subtend an angle of 1 second ?
2. Taking the mean distance of Mercury from the Sun as 37,000,000 miles, and the length of Mercury's year as 88 of our days, show that the speed of Mercury in her orbit is slightly less than $\frac{1}{8000}$ lux per second. [1 lux $\fallingdotseq$ 186,000 miles.]
3. It can be deduced from Einstein's space-time law that if the speed of a planet is v luxes per second, the major axis of its orbit advances $12v^2$ right angles per revolution. Using the data of No. 2, show that in 100 of our years the major axis of Mercury advances about 43 seconds.

4. With the data on p. 138, show that $\dfrac{8m}{\pi r}$ right angles is approximately 1·75 seconds.

5. Taking the radius of Jupiter as 43,000 miles, and its mass as $\frac{1}{1050}$ of that of the Sun, show that, according to the Einstein theory, the apparent displacement of a star so placed that the light-ray to the Earth just touches Jupiter's surface is about 0·017 second.

6. With the data on p. 136 for the spectral shift, prove that
$$\dfrac{t_1}{t_2} \fallingdotseq 1 \cdot 000002.$$

ANSWERS

EXERCISE I

3. 18·5.   **6.** 100 seconds.   **8.** 17 miles.   **9.** 39,800 stadia.

EXERCISE IIA

1. 4 feet.   **2.** 2 feet ; 6 inches.
3. 60 feet ; 3 inches ; 3 inches ; 4.
4. 2·6 inches ; 6 inches.   **5.** 0·25 ; $\frac{1}{4}=(\frac{1}{2})^2$.
6. Frustrum of pyramid, approx. $\frac{1}{2}$ by $\frac{1}{2}$ by $\frac{1}{4}$ inch.
7. 3 inches broad ; $\frac{3}{8}$ inch thick.   **8.** Too thin.

EXERCISE IIB

3. (i) Ordinary ; (ii) dial oval ; hands expand and contract
   as they rotate.
4. As in 3 (ii).   **5.** $63\frac{1}{2}°$ N. of E.   **6.** No.

EXERCISE III

1. 10 yards ; 24 yards.   **2.** $\frac{3}{4}y$ feet ; $\frac{4}{3}z$ feet.
3. 9 seconds ; 27 feet.   **4.** 20 seconds ; 25 seconds.
5. 32 feet.   **6.** Bullet ; together ; noise.

EXERCISE IV

1. (i) P 20, A 16, C 10 ; (ii) P 25, A 20, C 14 seconds past zero.
2. (i) P 30, A 24, C 15 ; (ii) P $37\frac{1}{2}$, A 30, C 21 seconds past zero.
3. (i) D 12 ahead of A ; (ii) 15.
4. (i) P 5, A 4, C 10 ; (ii) P 25, A 20, C 26 seconds past zero.
5. (i) Event at A ; (ii) event at C.   **6.** Yes.   **7.** 40 legs.

EXERCISE V

1. $\frac{4}{5}$ foot when pointing east ; loses 12 minute-spaces per
   hour ; A says the same about O.
2. A is 1·4 second-spaces ahead of C ; D is 2·8 second-spaces
   ahead of A ; A 24, C 22·6, D 26·8 seconds past zero.
3. $8\frac{1}{2}$ seconds ; $7\frac{1}{2}$ luxes.   **4.** 4 seconds ; same place.

EXERCISE VI

2. Yes ; $-\frac{1}{3}$; 11·3.   **3.** $x = 5\frac{1}{3}$, $t = 6\frac{2}{3}$; 4.

4. 9 luxes ; 12 ; $\frac{7}{25}$ or $-\frac{4}{5}$ lux per second.

5. 4 seconds, 7 luxes ; $-\frac{1}{4}$ second ; A says II. occurs before I. ;
$\sqrt{-33}$.

6. Imaginary ; indeterminate.   **7.** Real ; fixed.   **8.** Yes.

9. III. occurred after I. and II. ; no time-order exists for
I. and II.

10. 25 hours ; o.

EXERCISE VII

1. 84.   **2.** 1·6, 3·8, 10·4 ; (2·5, 5, 14 ; 77·5).

3. 84 seconds ; parallel to time-axis ; proper time.

5. 160.   **6.** 16 ; $8 + \sqrt{28} = 13·29$; no.

EXERCISE VIII

1. $\frac{4}{5}$, $\frac{28}{29}$ lux per second.   **2.** o, $\frac{8}{11}$ lux per second.

3. $\frac{2}{5}$ lux per second perp. to AB ; $\frac{3}{5}$ lux per second along AB.

4. $2\frac{1}{2}$, 3·75.   **5.** $1\frac{1}{2}$, 3·17.

EXERCISE IX

1. Yes ; a parabola ; a straight line.

2. B says the glass box first stops and then moves with
upward increasing vertical acceleration.

3. Yes.   **5.** o·ooo,oo5.   **6.** o·ooo,ooo,ooo,o15.

EXERCISE X

1. 3·26 miles.